The Sword of the Spirit

The Story of William Tyndale

by Joyce McPherson

To my grandchildren: may the word of God dwell in you richly.

Internet: www.greenleafpress.com

Table of Contents

Chapter 1

For God loued so the world; that he gaf his oon bigetun sone, that eche man that bileueth in him perisch not; but haue euerlastynge liif.

–John 3:16 as translated by John Wycliffe

Nibley Knoll

"Faster!"

William raced after his older brother Edward who was already halfway to the top of Nibley Knoll. Beyond the hill the sky blazed blue in the summer sunshine. A stiff breeze carried the smell of newly-turned earth, and William imagined that he was being swept by the breeze up the steep knoll.

"Faster!" His breath burned in his chest, and he saw Edward pause to look back. In that moment William spurted ahead and grasped the coarse grass at the top of the hill.

Edward dropped beside William. "You are getting faster every time. Soon father will think you are big enough to go to school."

William gulped in the fresh air. "I'm not going to school. I'm going to be a knight like Grandfather Tyndale."

"Knights have to go to school first," replied Edward. "They have to read letters from the King of England and send messages to their men." He motioned beyond the knoll to the rolling fields. "Look-- this is the way our grandfather crossed the Cotswolds to settle here."

William picked up the familiar tale. "Aye, he was weary and hungry, and he happened on this valley."

"But it was dangerous for his true identity to be known because he and the other knights were defeated in the War of the Roses, so he changed his name to Hutchins." Edward ended in a whisper. "He only revealed his true name to his children on his deathbed."

"Father is not afraid to use the name Tyndale when he trades his wool in London," said William.

"That's because it was long ago," explained Edward. "When I am a man like Father I will call myself by our true name, Tyndale."

William looked back at the green ridges falling away at his feet. "But I will always be a Hutchins," he said.

The boys sat on the top of the knoll and gazed down on the tidy village below. The stone houses glowed warmly in the sunshine. Beyond the cluster of homes and shops, the spire of the church reached humbly to heaven. A little farther a clear stream ran past the mill to the prosperous farms with their rich fields and pastures dotted with sheep. Grandmother liked to say, "As sure as God's in Gloucestershire."

William thought God must surely be in Gloucestershire today. Soon it would be the year of our Lord 1500, and some people said the world would end. William wondered if this was true. Fifteen hundred was a large number. There were probably not 1500 sheep in all the farms of Nibley.

Edward interrupted William's thoughts. "Let's race home!" Before William could answer, Edward darted down the hill. William raced after him as fast as he could.

Summer was especially long in Gloucestershire that year. William spent his days with Franz who herded sheep on the Tyndale property. Franz was a large man with curly black hair and a broad smile. He wore sturdy boots and a shepherd's smock which William greatly admired. He hoped his father would allow him to wear boots and a smock like Franz one day.

Franz came from Germany, and William had learned to speak his language as he followed the shepherd in the fields. William liked to hear Franz tell tales of his homeland and the sparkling Rhine River where beautiful maidens guarded a golden ring. Franz also taught William how to care for sheep and how to keep them from harm.

Sometimes William hunted blackberries, and there were always oxe-eye daisies and purple clover to gather for his mother. Every Sunday there was church where the priest intoned mysterious words like *Paternoster quiesincaelis.* At haying time, William helped his father cut the sweet-smelling grass, which they stacked in fat, round bales. The days slipped by as easily as the thread on his mother's spinning wheel.

The trees were showing the first tints of gold, when William's mother announced that it was time for him to begin school.

"Couldn't I stay here and help you?" he asked.

His mother laid baby Margaret in her cradle and busily tied bread and cheese in a homespun cloth. "Why would you want to stay home when there is so much to learn?"

William leaned against the cradle and touched the baby's tiny hand. The infant grasped his finger and gurgled. "I think I like home better," William said.

His mother stopped her work and studied her son for a moment. "William, you will like school. You will learn to read and write, and so many things! They will teach you Latin, and you will be able to understand the priest at church when he reads and prays."

Reluctantly, William took the bread and cheese from his mother and followed Edward down the path to school. On either side a heavy mist rose from the stubbled fields. They soon reached the village of Wotton-under-Edge. Edward led the way to the grammar school, which Lady Berkeley had founded over one hundred years ago.

The school building stood beneath a large chestnut tree. William mounted two worn steps and found himself in a small room filled with rows of wooden benches. Edward told him to sit with the youngest children. William sat on his bench and wondered what would happen next.

Suddenly the door opened and a young man entered the room. He walked with a slight limp and one shoulder hung lower than the other. Immediately the hum of conversation stopped, and William realized that this man must be the schoolmaster.

The schoolmaster walked slowly and deliberately to his desk and carefully laid three books on it. He turned to the class and announced: "There are hundreds and hundreds of books in the Oxford Library, but only a few dozen are in English. If you want to read the wisdom of the past or the ideas of the great men of our day, you must know Latin."

William tried to remember everything the schoolmaster said that first week. There was much to learn: letters and numbers and strange words that were supposed to be Latin. The classroom was noisy as all the students read aloud at once.

By the second month William could sound out the words that the professor gave him. Next came the laborious task of committing the grammar to memory. There were eight parts of speech and all of them had rules. In addition to grammar, the schoolmaster taught arithmetic and history.

The history class captured William's imagination. The schoolmaster told the students how the Romans came to England over 1400 years ago. They brought the Latin language and later, Christianity. Then the heathen Saxons came during the sixth century. They murdered the monks and burned the churches, but they could not stop people from believing in God.

The faithful Christians fled to the land beyond the Severn river. "Our Severn," thought William to himself. Late in the sixth century a man named Augustine converted King Ethelbert and preached in the south of England. To this day England was a Christian nation. William imagined King Ethelbert and his brave knights following a flag with a great cross. He decided he would be a Christian knight, too.

One day Edward and William did not have school. Harvest Sunday was coming and the school children brought vegetables to decorate the church. They spread fresh rushes on the floor and arranged their offerings in neat piles at the front of the sanctuary. On Sunday they were to come dressed in their best clothes so that they could carry garlands of flowers for a procession.

When the boys returned home, their grandmother was pulling a golden loaf of bread from the oven. "Come sit with me," she invited them. She placed a red cloth neatly across the table and cut thick slices of bread for the boys. Their little brother John ran from the next room where their mother was singing at her spinning. John was fair-haired like all the Tyndales, and he had the same dark brown eyes as his older brothers.

"I want some, too," he said. Grandmother took him on her lap and gave each of the children their portion.

As William chewed his bread, he ran his fingers over the soft red cloth on the table. His grandmother smiled at him.

"This cloth belonged to my grandmother," she said. "Your mother's people have been cloth merchants for generations, and today I will tell you a story about the cloth merchants."

William loved Grandmother's stories. Even John stopped wriggling to listen. Grandmother began in her sing-song voice. "It was cloth merchants who first took the Scripture in English from town to town. There were just a few pages with verses of the Bible copied on them, but they spread through Gloucestershire faster than a river at flood tide. Men read and memorized these verses and became followers of a man called Wycliffe."

"What did the followers do?" asked Edward.

"They traveled the countryside sharing the Scripture with everyone they met. They always wore long russet gowns. My father called them the poor priests." Grandmother chuckled. "Some people called them Lollards because they were always singing hymns: la-la-la."

William laughed. "That sounds like Edward milking the cows."

Grandmother continued. "Though they were outlawed as heretics, they kept preaching and teaching in secret. Many were burned at the stake. Years later the Bishop of Lincoln even had Master Wycliffe's bones removed from their grave so that he would not have a Christian burial. My father told me they burned his bones and threw the ashes into the River Swift."

"Into the river?" echoed John.

"Aye, and that river runs to the Avon which runs to the Severn and then to the sea. His ashes are scattered far and wide, like the Scripture he translated."

"Do you know any Scripture, Grandmother?" asked William.

Grandmother leaned forward and her voice came in a whisper. "I know them as my mother and father taught me. When my father was a boy, there was a law made that the Bible could only be read in Latin, so we were taught to be careful." Still speaking softly she recited. "For God loved so the world; that he gave his own begotten son, that each man that believeth in Him perish not; but have everlasting life."

William liked the way the words sounded, but what did it mean to have "everlasting life?"

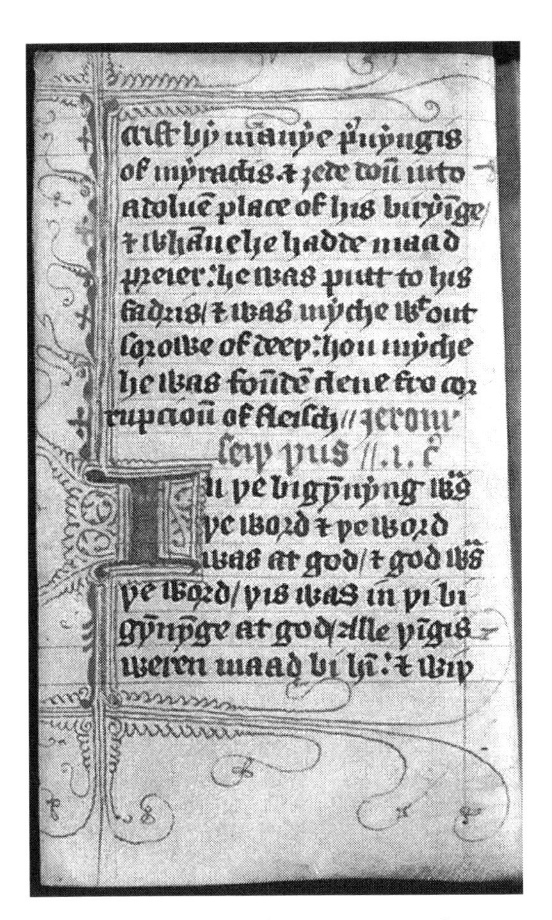
Aftir þe manye prechingis
of myraclis. & ȝede doun into
a dolue place of his biryinge
& whanne he hadde maad
preier: he was putt to his
fadris/ & was myche wiþout
sorowe of deeþ: hou myche
he was founden clene fro cor
rupcioun of fleisch // Jerom
seiþ þus //.i.c
In þe bigynnyng was
þe word & þe word
was at god/ & god was
þe word/ þis was in þe bi
gynnynge at god/ alle þingis
weren maad bi him: & wiþ

a handwritten copy of
Wycliffe's English translation
of the Gospel of John

Chapter 2

For alle men synneden, and han nede to the glorie of God.
--Romans 3:23 as translated by John Wycliffe

A Lollard Song

In winter the days were so short that William and Edward walked home in the chilly dusk as the first stars twinkled above the fields. At home they hurried through their chores. Edward milked the cows while William pitched the sweet-smelling hay into the mangers.

Each day the barnyard cats purred and rubbed against William's legs as he carried the large buckets of milk. He would scoop a bowl of milk for them and take the rest to the dairy, where his mother would make butter and cheese.

After dinner the family sat snug around the fire while Father told stories about the day's work and Mother sewed or knitted. Sometimes Mother would sing folk songs in her clear high voice.

One evening William and Edward sat on an old chest and toasted bits of bread over the fire. William liked to eat his toast with pieces of golden cheese that melted in mellow sweetness in his mouth. John sat nearby, sorting his collection of smooth rocks that he had found in the stream.

"Tonight I'm going to sing a song that my grandmother taught me," said their mother. The boys listened as she sang:

Hope thou in the Lord,
And do thou goodness.
Inhabit thou the land,
And thou shalt be fed with His riches
Delight thou in the Lord
And He shall give to thee
The askings of thine heart.
Show thy way to the Lord, and hope thou in Him,
And He shall do, and he shall lead out
thy rightfulness as light
And thy doom as midday.
Be thou subject to the Lord, and pray thou Him.

Grandmother listened with her eyes closed. At the end of the song she beckoned to the boys. "That was one of the Lollard songs," she said softly.

"Sing it again," they urged their mother. Their mother began again, and William listened to the lilting tune mingling with the gentle creaking of the rocking chair. Margaret fell asleep on his mother's lap, the child's tousled hair making a yellow halo around her face.

"Hope thou in the Lord," William repeated to himself. He wondered if that was the secret to the everlasting life in grandmother's Scripture verse.

The next day at school the song stuck in William's head. He was humming it to himself as he ate his lunch, when one of the big boys gave him a shove.

"You don't sing that kind of rubbish at school," he snarled.

William looked up in surprise at the boy's red face and sneering eyes.

"It's just a tune I heard," faltered William.

"It's Lollard rubbish," shouted the boy, giving William another push. "You can be burned at the stake for singing it."

Edward heard the commotion, and wedged himself between the boy and his brother. "Do you want to fight?" he asked sternly.

Edward was taller than the boy, who quickly decided to take a few steps back. "Just make sure your little brother doesn't bring his foul songs to school," he shouted and ran away.

William and Edward finished their lunch in silence, though William could still hear the song in his head.

One chilly spring day the rain rattled the single window in the school house, and William gripped his pen with numb fingers. Though the fire was lit, it produced more smoke than heat. William gazed at the smoldering fireplace and imagined the smoke rising over battles of old. The enemy hoards looked a lot like the red-faced boy.

The schoolmaster rapped his desk with his stick and all eyes turned to him. Those who were reading aloud immediately grew quiet.

"Our history lesson today will be Alfred the Great, who lived over six hundred years ago and was one of the greatest kings," the schoolmaster began. "Do you know why he is called 'great'?"

He looked sharply at his class to make sure they were

listening. "He created schools and promoted Christianity. This is even more remarkable when I tell you that he learned to read and write after he was a grown man. He paid scholars at his court to copy Scripture verses into a little book that he carried with him so that he could study."

William turned his head slightly to look at the red-faced boy, who scowled at him. William quickly looked back at the schoolmaster.

When the schoolmaster spoke of history, he seemed to grow straighter and taller. He walked before the students, waving his hands dramatically. "When Alfred the Great revised the laws of his kingdom, he added the Ten Commandments at the beginning. He also translated many of the Psalms from Latin to Anglo-Saxon." He added so quietly that only William and the students on the first row could hear. "Sadly, they are all lost now."

After school William and Edward walked home along the path where the leaves glistened after the rain. William listened to the drops which still fell from the tree branches.

"Edward, did you hear what the schoolmaster said about Alfred the Great copying Scripture verses into his little book?"

"Aye, Grandmother would like that story."

"Do you think King Alfred had the verse grandmother taught us about everlasting life?"

Edward gave this careful consideration. "Perhaps he did. We can be like King Alfred and copy that verse in our book."

"And the Lollard's song, too. Grandmother said that it was a Psalm of David."

At home the comfortable smell of roasted lamb and baked apples filled the great room where Grandmother sat carding wool. She listened intently to the story of Alfred the Great.

"The schoolmaster is right to say King Alfred was *great*," she said. "The written Scripture is one of the most precious things in the world."

Grandmother laid down her wool and took a small piece of parchment from a shelf on the wall. "Here is one of my greatest treasures. My father gave it to me. It is the only written piece of Scripture we have."

William took the parchment and read slowly: "For all men sinned and have need to the glory of God."

"You read well," said Grandmother with a smile of approval. "I want you to study your Latin so you can make me more Scripture like this."

William copied the Scripture in his book with the other verses. He thought for a long time about the new verse. Perhaps sin was the reason that God sent His son.

Summer came again. William sat on the stone wall, and breathed in the smell of the honeysuckle, whose long streamers waved over the hedges. In the distance the fields were dotted with poppies. Soon harvest time would come, and he would not be here to help. He kicked his heels against the wall and wished he did not have to leave home.

Franz approached with a young lamb in his arms. "Why are you not at school?" he said with his broken accent.

"My school does not begin until next week," William said. "Father is sending me to a school in Oxford, and I have come to say good-bye."

Franz nodded toward the sheep. "We are going to make a shepherd of you, *ja*?"

"I will come back," said William, "but Father says I must go away to school first."

"You won't forget your German, and how to talk with old Franz?" the shepherd queried.

"No, I must remember it so I can trade wool and cloth one day."

"*Gut*. You will come back then," Franz said confidently.

Chapter 3

Study to shew thyself laudable unto God
a workman that needeth not to be ashamed,
dividing the word of truth justly.
--II Timothy 2:15 as translated by William Tyndale

Pater Noster

William's father brought him to the town of Oxford where he would live for the next four years. The school stood in the midst of an impressive jumble of buildings.

William admired the intricately-carved stone towers and ornate spires. Father showed him the Magdalen Tower which had been completed only a few years ago. He placed his strong hand on William's shoulder. "I want you to study well and learn all that you can in this place," he said. "Here you will learn what you need so that you can take your place in the world."

William thought of home and was not sure that he wanted to take a place in the world. His father smiled. "I will come for you at the end of the school year. You can spend the summer with Franz and the sheep."

The headmaster placed William in the second form since he already knew the eight parts of speech and the pronunciation of Latin. Most of the boys were a little older than William: around eleven to twelve years of age.

The Magdalen Tower

William sat on his bench the first day and savored the smell of leather books and ink. He soon discovered that the classes at his new school were much more difficult than his grammar school classes. He had to work hard to keep up with the older boys.

The students received a rigorous education in preparation for attending college at the University of Oxford. Early school began in the frosty dimness of morning at six o'clock. At nine o'clock the students broke for breakfast. Afterwards they attended school again from quarter of ten to noon. Dinner followed, with afternoon school from one o' clock to five o'clock.

By the second month of school the boys were expected to speak Latin and translate simple sentences. If they could not recite their homework flawlessly, the schoolmaster required hundreds of lines to be copied. After his first stint at copying, William vowed he would not let his homework lapse again.

The busy days were broken by holy days and saints' days which kept the boys in happy anticipation of a break from school. November first was All Saints Day and ten days later was Martinmas or St. Martin's Day. William knew that Franz and the other farm hands would be slaughtering cattle for winter meat as was the custom at Martinmas. Though Oxford was quickly becoming his home, William missed his family on market days when he saw the booths filled with farm onions or the famous Gloucester cheeses.

In addition to Latin, the boys studied French and German. Due to his ease in learning languages, William was quickly promoted to the third form. He began to study Aesop's fables in Latin. His schoolmaster promised that by the end of the year they would read writings by a Roman named Terence.

Every year on May first, there was a ceremony of a requiem mass for the soul of Henry VII. The students in their scholar robes filed solemnly into the church. The schoolmaster watched the boys carefully.

"You must be on your best behavior," he explained in his clipped tones. "The soul of King Henry VII will leave purgatory and reach heaven sooner because of this mass."

William wondered how the priests would know when King Henry VII was done with purgatory.

After the mass, Morris Dancers played tabors and pipes, and danced in the streets. They wore flowers on their hats and leather patches rimmed with bells that jingled merrily. William listened to the bells and music, and questions about purgatory slipped away.

On Sundays when the students attended church William found that he could understand the Latin which the priest spoke. The mysterious words of his childhood: *Pater noster qui es in caelis* were actually a prayer. They meant: *Our Father, who art in heaven.* William listened carefully to the rest of the prayer until he understood all of it.

One day the priest intoned the words of the twenty-third Psalm. "The Lord is my shepherd." William thought of Franz and the way he taught him to take care of sheep. "He makes me lie down in green pastures." With a shiver of delight William understood each word. "Surely goodness and mercy shall follow me all the days of my life and I shall dwell in the house of the Lord forever." At that moment William knew that he wanted to follow that Shepherd with all his being.

After his first year of school William went home for several weeks. He reveled in the familiarity of primroses growing thickly on the banks, apple orchards in blossom, and the old blackbird that still had its nest in a hollow tree.

William's father took him to town to sell the fleeces after the spring clip. William listened with fascination to the merchants who spoke French and Dutch. Father spoke with them fluently in their languages, and William tried to understand as much as he could. As he stood by his father's side, William drank in the village sights: the stone cottages with tile roofs, the weaver's house where villagers took their woven cloth, and the market cross in the midst of stalls piled high with farm vegetables. It was good to be home.

Each evening around the big oak table, he told his family about the things he had learned at school. A new map had just been published. It included the lands of the New World with the suggestion that it be called *America* in honor of Amerigo Vespucci. Vespucci explored the coast of the New World and discovered that it was much larger than Christopher Columbus had imagined.

The new school year started and William was in the fourth form. The schoolmaster required the students to read Virgil's *Aeneid*. He coached the boys to speak the words of Virgil *voce ben sonora* to bring out the majesty of his poetry. William read the opening lines over and over again: *Arma virumque cano.* He translated: *Of arms and of a man, I sing.*

The high words filled him with a delicious sense of greatness and power. He could see the high walls of Troy besieged by the army of the Greeks. Brave Hector would lead forth the Trojan army, and crafty Odysseus would...

"Can anyone tell me the principal parts of *cano*?" The schoolmaster's voice cut sharply through William's reverie. He looked up in time to see the teacher's piercing gaze resting on him.

William promptly stood next to his desk and recited: "*cano, canere, cecini*, meaning *to sing.*"

As he sat down again, he thought about the word *cano, to sing.* Virgil made his words to sing. Perhaps that was why the writing stirred his soul.

One afternoon William's father visited him. "I've brought you some of your mother's apple tarts," he said as he produced a small parcel wrapped with string.

William bit into the sugary crust and listened happily to the news his father brought from home.

"Edward has joined me in the cloth trade, and John has begun grammar school," he said. He asked about William's courses and was interested to learn that he was studying a history book by William of Malmesbury.

"Ah, the kings of England. I studied this book when I was in school. Have you read about my favorite, King Athelstan?"

"He was the grandson of Alfred the Great," said William. "And he set up lots of schools."

His father nodded in approval. "He also had the Bible translated into the language the people spoke in that day."

De Oratore

William thought of the Lollard's Scripture that his grandmother hid so carefully. A lot had changed since the time of King Athelstan.

By Christmas William entered the fifth form, where the students studied *De Oratore* by Cicero. Cicero did not write his advice as a textbook. Instead he created a story about a discussion among several Romans. As scattered snowflakes danced among the spires of Oxford, William read about a lush Italian garden where gifted Romans met to discuss what makes a great orator. William translated:

> *The complete and perfect orator is he who can speak in public about every subject with richness of arguments and variety of tunes and images.*

William copied in his notebook the five steps of the orator:

Inventio, which required finding the arguments
Dispositio, which required sorting the arguments in logical order
Elocutio, which meant using ornate speech and rhetorical devices
Memoria, which meant memorizing the speech
Actio, which meant using dignity, voice modulation and gesture to present the speech

Cicero taught that even more important than skill, was virtue. The perfect orator must be a moral guide to his people.

The schoolmaster required the students to translate from Latin and back again to build their skills. "You will find better words," the schoolmaster told the class. "And perhaps if you are very clever, you may be able to create a new word or phrase that will appeal to your audience. This is called a neologism."

The schoolmaster liked to recite to his students: "*Stilus optimus et praestantissimus dicendi effector ac magister.* The pen is the best and most efficient creator and master of speaking."

Another summer came and William returned home. He sat at the broad oak table and breathed in the spicy smell of gooseberry pies baking in their raised crusts. After a year at school, William could almost feel the rich scents of home filling the hollow spaces inside, just as his mother's hearty dinners filled his stomach.

Margaret sat by William's side and proudly showed him how she could card wool. "Feel how soft it is," she said as she patted the growing pile.

The door flew open and John ran in, a great smile on his freckled face. "Franz says there are two more lambs born in the night!"

William followed John to the fields where a dozen wooly lambs frisked near the mother sheep. Holding the new lambs in his arms, William spoke softly, "The Lord is my shepherd—I shall not want. He makes me to lie down in green pastures. He leads me beside still waters. He restores my soul."

Franz, whose hair had turned silver while William was away, leaned on his shepherd's staff. "What is that you say?"

William repeated the words for Franz. "It's from the Psalms of David," he explained.

Franz' weathered face lit up in recognition. "*Das ist gut.* The Lord is my shepherd. This I have always known."

When William returned to Oxford, he was in the sixth form. It was a strange feeling to realize that he was one of the older students now. The sixth form studied Caesar's Gallic War.

"*Gallia est omnis divisa in partes tres.*" The new schoolmaster pronounced each word slowly. As William carefully copied the words, he imagined Caesar preparing to face the various tribes: provisioning the troops and constructing fortresses. Then the battles come, with Caesar and his legions facing thousands of men. The cavalry breaks the line...

A splotch of ink stained his writing, and William rushed to blot it and keep up with the class. By the end of the dictation, his fingers were cramped from writing.

"You will translate the first chapter into English for tomorrow," the schoolmaster ended abruptly.

In his last year of preparatory school, William's teachers required the students to take a passage and translate from Latin to English and then back into both Latin prose and poetry. William relished the challenge and even tried his hand at creating some neologisms.

William's days were so full of study that even the last moment of the day was used to memorize passages that would be recited the next day. William often reviewed the Latin words of the Lord's Prayer and the Apostle's Creed which were recited in church each week. Now that he could understand their meaning, they filled him with an overpowering sense of beauty: *Thy kingdom come; thy will be done...*" God was our Father, but He was also the king of a kingdom. And one day His kingdom would come.

Chapter 4

For all Scripture given by inspiration of God,
is profitable to teach, to improve, to amend and to instruct
in righteousness, that the man of God may be perfect
and prepared unto all good works.

-- II Timothy 3:16 as translated by William Tyndale

Chopological Sense

At last it was time for William to enter the university at Oxford. He lived in Magdalen Hall near the university library. William remembered how his schoolmaster in grammar school told them of hundreds of books housed in this library. He was curious to see them for himself.

As he entered his first lecture hall, he met a student named John Dorne, who seemed eager to talk. He introduced himself, shaking hands briskly. “I’m here at Oxford for two reasons, and one is that Oxford is the best place to study logic,” he told William.

He asked William his name, and when he learned that he was from Gloucestershire, he cocked his head to the side. “Wycliffe territory. Have you heard of him?”

"Of course," answered William. "My grandmother spoke of him often. She even had a piece of Scripture that he translated."

John broke into a grin that spread across his face. "John Wycliffe was a Fellow here and then became the Master of Balliol College. His work with the Scripture is the second reason that I am here."

As the scarlet berries ripened on the holly bushes and the sycamore leaves turned crimson, William and John learned arithmetic, logic, geometry and astronomy. They read Priscian, Aristotle, Boethius, Euclid, and Ptolemy. In Latin class they also studied a small section of the Vulgate, which was the Latin translation of the Bible. For every few words of the Scripture the teacher would dictate pages of commentary written over the last eleven hundred years.

William grew impatient as he studied the pages of notes. "Have you noticed that the commentators chop up the text and expound it twenty different ways?" he asked John.

John looked up from his pages with a dazed expression. "Did you say chop?"

"I call this the chopological sense of the passage."

John's eyes focused and he registered William's words. "Ha! Chopological-- that is a good term."

William and John decided to piece together the words from the books in the library. They had to be careful, because the formal study of theology was forbidden during undergraduate studies.

They began with the gospel of Saint John. They were pleased to find that a clear meaning began to emerge. "A pity it's buried under piles of commentary," William declared. Each day he carefully added to his translation of the gospel.

When he reached the third chapter, he found the verse

his grandmother had taught him: *For God loved so the world...* He carefully translated the next verse: *For God sent not his son into the world, to condemn the world; but that the world through him might be saved. He that believeth on him, shall not be condemned.*

What a wonderful thing-- Jesus, the son, came to save us! As William drank in the truth of God's word, he had an idea.

That summer when William went home, he traveled the last part on foot, the better to savor the familiar countryside with its rounded hills and fertile farms. Flowers grew along the lane and among the hedgerows that fringed the fields. As he neared his home on the side of Stinchcombe Hill, William saw the sun setting in golden glory beyond the green hills.

His grandmother greeted him warmly from her chair by the fire. William bent to kiss her and at the same time let a packet fall into her lap.

"This is a translation of the gospel of Saint John," he told her. "It's for you."

His grandmother touched it reverently. William opened the packet and turned to the third chapter. "Look here, grandmother. There is more of the verse you taught me." He read in his sonorous voice while his grandmother listened with a faraway look in her eyes.

When he finished she whispered. "I will treasure it always."

The second year at the University William studied Greek under William Latimer. With his red woolen neck warmer wound around his throat, he looked more like a grandfather than a distinguished scholar. When William first heard him teach, however, he knew that he had found one of the great scholars of Oxford. Professor Latimer was a friend of Erasmus, and he encouraged the students to read

Erasmus' book, *The Praise of Folly*.

In John Dorne's room, William sat amidst a half dozen cats who dozed in the autumn sunshine.

"What do you think of Erasmus' new book?" asked John.

William was reading the copy John had borrowed from a friend. "It is quite witty, but perhaps a little insulting to those churchmen who love the world more than Christ."

John's face twitched into a smile, and he snatched the book from William. "Listen to this part!" He read in Latin: *"Now, as for the popes, who act in Christ's place, if they tried to imitate his way of life-- namely poverty, labor, teaching, the cross, contempt of the world-- ... who on earth could be more miserable? How many advantages would these men be deprived of if they were ever assailed by wisdom."*

"I wonder what Professor Latimer thinks of Erasmus' opinions," said William.

"My grandfather says that it is a shame the way the clergy make themselves rich and care nothing for their people," said John.

"There must be a way to set things right," said William, who was now covered by cats purring contentedly. "The more we study the Scripture, the more clearly I understand my own faith. Perhaps that is what the church needs."

John was doubtful. "If we have to study in secret, do you think it is likely that the church will promote Scripture study?"

At Oxford a new craze had captured the students' attention. A fencing master from London had set up a school and offered lessons for a modest fee. William could only afford a few lessons, but he often practiced with other students. It was a welcome break from hours spent studying.

The second-year students were reading Cicero's *De Inventione*. William's professor liked to remind the students that Cicero had written: "To teach is a necessity, to delight is a beauty, to persuade is a triumph."

"I want you to be eloquent in your speeches, for one day you may have to persuade statesmen for some great cause," he told them.

The professor used authors from antiquity as models for speeches and compositions. He showed the students the figures and tropes of rhetoric that they used. After class the students spent hours writing their own essays using these methods.

William enjoyed trying to fit as many figures as possible into his work. It was like mental fencing: attack-defend-attack again. One of his favorite devices was called *reductio ad absurdum*, in which the writer extended an idea to an absurd conclusion.

William thought of the hundreds of clergymen in England who were busy selling Masses to deliver souls from Purgatory. Using *reductio ad absurdum*, one might say that if they were really accomplishing what they claimed, Purgatory would be empty.

By March the yew trees were shaking off the last of their mantle of snow. In his mind's eye, William could see the willow catkins of Gloucestershire showing white and the first daffodils pushing up green stalks through the earth.

One day Professor Latimer asked William and John to meet him after the lecture. Tugging his neck warmer tightly, he gave them his best grandfatherly stare. "I've been watching the two of you and I would like to suggest that you concentrate your studies in the Greek language. It is the original language of the Scripture, and could change your future work."

William looked at John and wondered whether the professor knew about their secret studies of the Latin Bible.

"When old dean Colet brought Greek to Oxford, great changes began," continued the professor.

"What kind of changes?" asked William, hoping to deflect any discussion of Bible studies.

"Colet taught the extraordinary idea that the simple sense of the Greek was the correct understanding of the Scripture." Professor Latimer paused and William could tell that he enjoyed having an audience.

"Why was that extraordinary?" said John.

"Well, among scholars it was believed that to understand Scripture, one must study all the allegories for each word. Animals mentioned in Scripture, for example, represented certain virtues. One also must study figures of speech that might suggest other meanings or morals. There are texts of Scripture that are dwarfed by the centuries of notes that have been added by various scholars."

"I've read some of them," said William.

Professor Latimer gave him an appraising glance. "Then you will understand how important it was to teach that the sense of the New Testament is wholly literal."

John gave a low whistle. "That would save me a lot of time in my studies. I have been up all night studying how Jerusalem is not only the city of the Jews, but is also an allegory for the Church or a symbol of the human soul or a reference to the future heavenly city!"

William spoke slowly. "It is true that Scripture uses symbols and metaphors, but the problem arises if every time you see a certain word, you think you have to haul in every single meaning and make it fit. Some of the commentaries we have studied are ridiculous!"

"That's the greatest cause of the decay of the faith," said Professor Latimer. "These scholars believe that

Scripture is a tool for making up all kinds of foolish allegories. With a theme of half an inch they draw a thread nine days long."

John laughed. "William calls that the chopological sense!"

The professor chuckled as he gathered up his papers. "We need a new generation of scholars who will put the pieces back together."

After their talk with the professor, John and William spent more time on their Greek studies. They learned that there were lectures on Greek for upper classmen, which they began attending.

One day John stopped William after class. "I've been talking with Professor Latimer again. Did you know that Erasmus went to Oxford to hear those lectures of old dean Colet in 1499? Some say that he first set the goal of editing the New Testament in Greek at that time. He has been working on it for years but it hasn't been printed yet."

"Erasmus is doing this?" said William in surprise. He had read the most recent book by Erasmus which was called *Adages*. It was a collection of famous sayings from classical literature and one of the most popular books in Europe. "His Greek New Testament will rival even his *Adages*."

"If this is true, perhaps we should get ready," said John.

"What can we do?" asked William.

Erasmus

"You said there must be a way to set things right," said John. "Perhaps it is time to invite others to study Scripture with us."

In the weeks that followed William and John invited a few friends who seemed interested in the Bible. Word spread, and several students and fellows of Magdanlen College joined them for their study.

One evening William read from the Latin Bible: "*Lex per Moysen data est, gratia et veritas per Jesum Christum facta est*. That translates as 'the law was given through Moses, grace and truth were made through Jesus Christ.' Why were grace and truth needed?"

"We know the law is good," began one student hesitantly, "but it seems from what we read last week that no one can keep it perfectly."

Another student picked up the idea. "We need God's grace because we cannot come to God on our own merits."

"And we need the truth that Jesus brought," added William. "Without the truth, the church suffers."

The discussion was lively as the students rifled through their handwritten copies of Scripture passages to understand its teaching.

Chapter 5

But when we come to praise God, either in Himself, or in His works, what a field for beauty and splendor of language opens up before man, who can task his powers to the utmost in praising Him whom no one can adequately praise, though there is no one who does not praise Him in some measure!

--Augustine in *On Christian Doctrine*

Saint Augustine

On July 4, 1512, the registrar of the University of Oxford recorded that "William Hychyns" received his Bachelor of Arts from Magdalen Hall. The same year a physician named Copernicus published the revolutionary theory that the planets revolve around the sun.

William traveled home to ask his father for permission to continue his education. The next step would be preparation for the priesthood. William hoped to find the tools he needed to fulfill his growing desire to bring the Scripture in English to his country. His father was pleased with William's choice and sent him back to school.

For his next degree, William was required to have certain books. If he could not afford to buy them, he was expected to borrow the book or make a copy for himself from an "exemplar," which was a sample copy for students to use. He studied the three philosophies: natural, moral and metaphysical. In philosophy the authority was Aristotle, who lived three centuries before Christ. He was a Greek philosopher who wrote the first encyclopedia in an effort to systematically describe the natural world.

John and William toiled over the exemplar in the library to copy Aristotle's works. William rubbed his sore fingers. "There is something about Aristotle that bothers me."

John looked glum. "When you study the works alone, they make sense, but..."

"When you compare them to the Scripture, they seem incomplete," finished William.

The notion intrigued William and he promised himself that he would study it further. A few days later while reading Augustine's *City of God*, William found a startling idea. He rushed into John's room, scattering cats as he went. "Augustine knows the answer!"

"What answer," said John who had been half-asleep over his books only a moment before.

"The answer to why Aristotle seems incomplete. Augustine studied Aristotle before he came to faith in Christ, and later he wrote about it."

"And what did our revered Saint Augustine say?" said John taking the nearest cat to lie on his lap.

"Augustine wrote that the ancient philosophers wore out their minds and powers in seeking the causes of things."

"That sounds like a good description of myself," said John.

"But Christian men are better because they know God and have found the Cause by which the universe has been made." William paused for breath as the entire idea filled his head.

"John, the ancient philosophers could only provide a shadow of the truth. The ultimate truth is found in God alone!"

During the summer William returned to Gloucestershire. He savored his life at home: the wooden trenchers on the broad table, his mother carding wool in her rocker by the hearth, and the smell of meadowsweet through the open windows. William spent hours talking with his father about his studies.

"They say Scripture is so hard that it cannot be understood without the teachings of the ancients," explained William.

"Do you find this to be true, son?"

"I do not. To the contrary, some of the ancient teachings are nonsense. Even the great Aristotle often contradicts the Bible!"

"This troubles you?"

"Aye, because some of our professors are not content with the wholesome words of our Lord Jesus, but waste their brains about questions and strife of words."

"Ah, words." William's father nodded with understanding. "I have long known that the Church uses Latin like a kind of magic."

"The Latin words themselves have lost all meaning," continued William. "When a child is christened, they call it *volowing*, because the priest says, '*volo* say ye.' It would be plainer if the parents simply said '*I will*' in English."

"Does this mean you will quit your studies?" asked his father.

"No, I need to learn more than ever. Father, did you know that when St. Jerome translated the Bible into Latin, he did so because it was the language of the people? St. Jerome wrote that *ignorance of Scripture is ignorance of*

Christ."

William's father nodded slowly. "We need St. Jerome here in England."

When William returned to the university to continue his Masters degree, he learned that John Dorne had completed his studies. He had reached the age for ordination to the priesthood and would begin his work as a priest. William still had several years before he would be eligible. The two friends talked late into the evening about their plans for the future.

"What will you do after your Master of Arts?" John asked William.

"I have talked with my father, and I plan to go to Cambridge to prepare for ordination."

"Cambridge." John's eyes twinkled merrily. "Could it be that you want to study where the great Erasmus worked only a few years ago?"

"John, you know Cambridge has a reputation for teaching Greek."

"And you have a taste for studying a certain book that was written in Greek!"

At last on June 26, 1515 William was licensed as a Master of Arts. With great anticipation he packed his well-worn copies of St. Augustine and the Scripture and made his way to Cambridge.

The library at Cambridge held a treasure of documents. William spent as much time as possible studying ancient manuscripts with their yellowed pages and faded ink. One day the book by Augustine that he requested was already in use. The librarian pointed him to a scholar who was sitting across the room deep in study.

William saw a man about his age with a short beard and aquiline nose, which gave him a hawkish look. William hesitated to approach him, but the man looked up and his eyes sparkled with friendliness.

"You are a student of Augustine as well?" he said.

The two men introduced themselves, and William learned that his name was Thomas Bilney. He told William how Cambridge was known for promoting the concept of *ad fontes*-or *back to the sources*- which enabled students to seek foundational truths in the Bible.

Thomas Bilney

"It's common sense," he explained. "In canon law, which I study, there are laws which have authority because of the church. In the same way, the Scripture has authority because it is the word of God."

"Do you read the Scripture?" asked William.

Thomas checked to make sure that no one was listening. "I came to faith by reading the first chapter of I Timothy." He quoted reverently: "*This is a true saying and by all means worthy to be received, that Christ Jesus came into the world to save sinners.* When I first read this verse, I felt a marvelous comfort and quietness."

"I understand," said William. "For me it was the twenty-third Psalm."

William and Thomas met often over books in the library. William found his new friend to be an intense student, and he admired his wide-ranging interest in church history and canon law. He also found a listening ear when he wanted to talk about new truths he discovered in the Scripture. In 1516, the Greek New Testament published by Erasmus arrived at last, and William and Thomas bought two of the first copies.

As William held the heavy volume in his hands, he knew that he would read every letter. The first part of the book contained parallel columns of Erasmus' Latin translation beside the Greek. The title of each book was at the top of the page, but there were no divisions for verses or chapters.

The next section, entitled Annotations, contained essays in Latin that commented on various words and phrases. The Annotations were as thick as the New Testament itself.

William was enchanted with the new book. He enthusiastically showed passages to Thomas. "Listen to this from the preface! *Christ wishes his mysteries to be published as widely as possible. I would wish even all women to read the gospel and the epistles of St. Paul, and I wish that they were translated into all languages of all Christian people, that they might be read and known.*"

"I think there will not be as much competition for the Augustine manuscript for a long time," said Thomas.

At Cambridge the students were expected to learn from public debates. One evening William and Thomas attended a debate that promised to investigate the existence of God.

As William waited for the program to begin, he sat in the lecture hall and thought about a recent verse from the Greek New Testament that he had been translating: *For all Scripture given by inspiration of God is profitable to teach.* He was just beginning to explore the ramification of these words, when the dean rose to introduce the two clergymen who would be speaking.

The first man began reading from his notes in a gravelly voice. "Although being has many properties, I shall set forth in this first chapter the four divisions of order."

William listened as the scholar listed the four divisions. It was the old debate between Scotus and Aquinas as to whether essence and existence were distinct.

"I do not take essential order, however, in the strict sense as do some who say that what is posterior is ordered whereas what is first or prior transcends order," the gravelly voice droned on.

William looked at Thomas who was watching the proceedings with a growing frown.

"As the Scripture says," began the scholar. William leaned forward, but was disappointed to find that the passage had little to do with the subject. William began to mentally list the speaker's arguments and dream up better ways to say them.

"In conclusion," the clergyman said at last, "the cause mentioned in the first part of the second division is in turn divided into the famous fourfold classification of final, efficient, material and formal cause, which need no explanation."

William grinned at Thomas, who made a motion for them to leave before the next speaker began.

William came out into the fresh evening air and laughed aloud. "If that is the best that our clergy can do, then I think we all need to get back to studying the Scripture."

"I'm afraid that they fashion the Scripture after their own imagination, as a potter does his clay," replied Thomas.

"Like the debate last week. Out of the same text one proved purgatory, and another proved that an ape has a tail."

"And they are the ones who claim that reading Scripture will drive you mad," said Thomas.

As the two friends talked, they made their way down to the River Cam. William admired the great trees that lined the river. They reminded him that God was always at work, whether through creation or through His inspired word.

"The Bible says that all Scripture is given by inspiration of God and is profitable to teach," said William. "The English clergy should be the guides of light to the people, but they drive the people from the knowledge of the Scripture! They won't translate it themselves and they won't abide it to be translated by others."

Thomas nodded soberly. "Aye, they would keep the people in darkness so that they might control them with vain superstition and false doctrine."

Woodcut of scholars debating

William looked back at the fine stone buildings of the university and sighed. "What reverence we give to holy water, holy fire, holy ashes! I would rather have a steadfast faith and the Holy Ghost."

Chapter 6

In the universities they have ordained that no man shall look in the Scripture until he be noselled (nursed) in heathen learning eight or nine years and armed with false principles with which he is clean shut out of the understanding of Scripture.
--William Tyndale in *The Practice of Prelates*

The White Horse Inn

Snow fell softly throughout the day. It gilded the dark berries of the privet hedges and glistened in the pools of light that spilled from shop windows. William peered along the lane looking for a tavern sign.

Thomas had insisted that William come to the White Horse Inn to discuss the new books that were coming out of Germany. They were written by a man named Martin Luther.

The snow was falling more thickly and a bitter wind had arisen, when at last William spied the wooden sign painted with a white horse. He pushed open the heavy oak door and stepped into the room. A fire blazed on a wide hearth, and nearby a group of men sat talking in low voices. Thomas strode forward to introduce William to the other men.

"This is Friar Barnes," said Thomas, bringing William to a man in a monk's habit. "He has achieved the herculean task of improving learning at the Augustinian priory. Now he has the monks studying Paul's epistles."

William shook the friar's hand. "It is an honor to meet you, sir."

Next Thomas motioned to a tall man with a shock of black hair. "William, this is John Frith, one of our brilliant scholars."

John stood up and William found himself dwarfed by the young man who stood at least a head taller than the other men.

"Thomas has told us much about your studies," John said. "I am glad you could come."

Miles Coverdale

Finally, Thomas turned to a man whose deep brow and serious eyes gave him a solemn appearance. "And this is Miles Coverdale who has just returned from Germany where he acquired his doctorate degree."

Miles held up several small booklets. "I also acquired these," he said with a smile.

Friar Barnes offered William a chair. "We are reading the epistles of Saint Paul, and we have been challenged by the idea that salvation is by grace alone."

"For by grace you have been saved," said William.

The friar nodded in appreciation. "I see you have read the second chapter of the epistle to the Ephesians."

Miles pushed one of his booklets across to William. "Curiously, our discoveries are in accord with our brother Martin Luther in Germany."

The men talked late into the evening while the snow blanketed the town. The discussion of the Bible encouraged William. The men invited him to St. Edward's Church where the preachers taught from the Scripture. Over the next few months William drank in the rich ideas and stimulating conversations of his new friends.

At the end of 1520, the Cambridge officials became worried that Luther's books were so numerous and his ideas discussed so openly that the university would fall into disrepute. The officials rounded up as many of Luther's books as they could and burned them in a public display.

The men still met at the White Horse Inn, but they came through the back door. William realized how many true friends he had found there. There was tall John Frith with his angular frame and deep voice that took on the quality of thunder when a particular Scripture inspired him. There was Miles Coverdale, who liked to reference and cross-reference the Scripture as they studied. There were also enthusiastic men like Hugh Latimer, Thomas Cranmer, and Nicholas Ridley.

One wintry day Miles greeted the others with his brows knotted in concern. "The Pope issued a Papal Bull condemning Luther, and ordered his books to be burned," he announced.

"The Pope?" queried John. "It is one thing when the Cambridge officials burn books, but if the Pope opposes Luther, it will be dangerous for him."

Friar Barnes broke into the conversation. "I also heard that Luther had a public book burning of his own."

"He burned his own books?" William asked.

"No, he burned some books of canon law, some decrees by the pope and the Papal Bull itself! He said that what he burned was erroneous," said Friar Barnes with a chuckle.

Over the next few months Miles helped William prepare for ordination. They studied the epistle to the Ephesians together. William pondered the sixth chapter which exhorted believers to be strong in the Lord and to put on the armor of God. There were the breastplate of righteousness, the shoes of the gospel of peace, the shield of faith, the helmet of salvation and the sword of the spirit. The Scripture taught that the sword of the spirit was the word of God. William was determined to take up this sword.

At last in 1521 William was ordained to the priesthood. He wanted to preach, but he also needed a certain type of position. He went to his brother Edward for help.

Edward was now Crown Steward for the Berkeley estate which covered vast properties from Gloucestershire to London. He had taken over the post from Sir John Walsh, whose family had been friends with the Tyndale family for generations.

Edward was thoughtful when he heard William's request. "You need a quiet place to study and translate the New Testament? I think I have the place for you."

The next week William became tutor to the two young sons of Sir John Walsh at his estate of Little Sodbury in Gloucestershire.

Chapter 7

Take this as your fourth rule: that you set Christ before you as the only goal of your whole life and direct all your efforts, all your activities, all your leisure, and all your business in His direction.

--Erasmus in *Enchiridion Militis Christiani*

The Handbook of the Christian Knight

Little Sodbury Manor felt like home to William. The manor, with its Cotswold stone walls and tile roof, reminded him of his childhood home. His students, Johnny and Robert, were just beginning their education, which would give William plenty of time for his translation work.

Little Sodbury Manor

On his first morning William awoke in his small room in the eaves. The pure, sweet song of a thrush trilled through his open window. Leaning out of the window, William looked on stone steps that led to the manor's chapel. Beyond lay ridge upon ridge of Welsh mountains cloaked in early morning mist. It was March 1st, St. David's Day. The church year began with March, and William imagined that a new year was beginning for him as well.

Each day he tutored the boys in the morning. After a mid-day meal, he took the boys for a walk, and then worked on his translation during the late afternoon and evening.

One day he took the boys farther afield to the small lake on the manor estate. The elm trees were in bloom and spikes of daffodils waved above the grass. It was easy for William to imagine that he was a boy again.

Johnny, the older son of Sir John, tugged on William's coat. "Did you know that our grandfather was knighted at Bosworth Field?"

"Ah, that was a mighty battle," William said.

"When Robert and I grow up, we will be knights, too." Johnny broke into a gallop and his little brother, Robert, fell in behind him.

"Do you know the best kind of knight to be?" William asked.

The boys stopped their galloping to listen.

"The best kind of knight," William said, "is a Christian knight. I am reading a book about the Christian knight now."

The boys' eyes grew round. "Will you tell us what the book says?" Johnny asked.

William solemnly patted his heart. "The first step begins here," he said. "The Christian knight must love the Lord with all his heart."

During the summer William began preaching at St. Austin's Green, which was an open space in front of the Augustinian priory in Bristol. Like the priests in the churches, he would read the text in Latin, but then he would translate it into English and explain the meaning.

At first only a few townspeople attended, but soon more and more people came. They admired the earnest young preacher with his neatly trimmed beard and long professor's gown, who spoke so plainly in English. "He's not like the doctors from Oxford," they told each other. "He speaks the clear truth."

William received letters from his friend Miles Coverdale who was serving as a monk. Miles wrote that King Henry VIII had written a book against Martin Luther and received the title of *Fidei Defensor* or *Defender of the Faith* from the Pope. Miles also wrote about a man named Thomas More, who was a rising star in the government. He was rumored to have written large sections of the book for the king.

Little Sodbury Manor was only ten miles south of Stinchcombe and William's brother, Edward, often came to visit. Edward went by the name of Tyndale now.

One day he seemed anxious when he came to visit. "William, I have heard about your preaching and I believe much good will come of it."

"Thank you," said William. "But I see that you are troubled about something."

"Unfortunately some of the clerics are suspicious of you. They say you preach in English and your words are like Luther's."

"My words are from the Scripture."

Edward was not satisfied. "Did you hear that Cardinal Wolsey ordered books by Luther to be burned? He had a great ceremony and sat in his chair under a canopy of gold cloth."

"I must answer like the Apostle Paul," William said gravely. "I am not ashamed of the gospel. It is the power of

God for salvation for everyone who believes. Even the cardinal must see that."

"I hope he does," said Edward, but his eyes were still filled with concern.

Sir John often invited clergymen to dine at Little Sodbury Manor. One autumn evening the local cleric paid them a visit. He had heard rumors about Sir John's new tutor and was disappointed to find he was not at dinner.

"You must excuse our tutor," Lady Ann told him. "He is so devoted to his books that he scarcely notices the time of day."

The cleric raised his eyebrows. "Is he then at liberty from instructing your children?"

Lady Ann exchanged a quick glance with her husband. "Surely, you do not expect our children to have their lessons into the evening?"

The man covered his embarrassment by coughing lightly into his handkerchief. "Certainly not, milady."

At this moment William himself appeared. He had hastily donned a dinner collar and scholar's robe. He bowed to Sir John and Lady Ann, then turned and bowed to the cleric.

The cleric nodded his head in curt approval. "I'm glad to see they still teach courtesy at Oxford," he said in the way of acknowledgment.

Sir John rose elegantly. "May I introduce William Hutchins, sometimes called Tyndale."

The cleric's eyebrows rose even higher so that they touched his close-fitting cap. "I know the Tyndale family. Are you related to Edward Tyndale, the Crown Steward for the Berkeley estate?"

William tried to hide his smile. "He's my brother."

"Ah, of course," he blustered. "Please excuse the

mistake, but I heard you were a recent graduate of Oxford and Cambridge, and a tutor."

"I am as you say," said William.

"And you are perhaps waiting for better prospects?" prompted the cleric politely.

William thought of the books awaiting him in his room. "I am," he said decisively.

The cleric appeared satisfied with his inquiries and turned to Sir John to discuss the poor state of collections for the church.

William was completely forgotten during the meal which followed. He allowed the conversation to flow around him like a quick-running Cotswold stream. He barely tasted the mutton and spring peas as he contemplated the slim book he was translating.

It was called the *Enchiridion Militis Christiani*, which he translated into English as *The Handbook of the Christian Knight*. It was written by Erasmus, the great Latin scholar.

In the book Erasmus taught how a Christian should live. He likened the Christian to a knight and described his two main weapons as prayer and knowledge of the Bible. William pondered the words he had just translated: "Faith is the only gate unto Christ."

As William chewed on these thoughts along with his food, he was dimly aware of Sir John's voice punctuating the conversation. His tone grew more insistent until William found himself listening.

"Surely you must admit that the Holy Scripture is the foundation of our faith," Sir John was saying.

The cleric waved a hand at him as though dismissing his last remark. "Nevertheless it would be wrong to translate the Holy Scripture into the English tongue."

"But if the people cannot understand the words of the

Scripture, it is like the words are locked away," William said. "Saint John wrote in his first letter 'These things have I written unto you that believe on the name of the son of God, that ye may know how that ye have eternal life.' How will they understand if the priest only reads in Latin?"

"You have no understanding of the Church," the cleric declared. "The Church itself is more important. We were better to be without God's words than the pope's!"

Before William considered carefully, he said, "I believe that with a little effort I could prepare a boy that drives the plow to know more of Scripture than you."

The cleric slowly turned red, and William decided it was a good time to excuse himself from dinner.

Chapter 8

In the first place, you should continually bear in mind that mortal life is nothing but a kind of perpetual warfare.

--Erasmus in *Enchiridion Militis Christiani*

On Trial

The next week, Sir John and Lady Ann were invited to dine with several high-ranking officials of the church. When the Walshes returned from dinner, they asked William to talk with them. They wanted to discuss the opinions that the educated men had put forth during dinner. William knew that both Sir John and Lady Ann were eager to know more, so he showed how certain opinions were contrary to God's word.

Lady Ann listened politely, but she seemed amused at William's confidence. "There was a doctor who spends two hundred pounds by the year. Another spends one hundred pounds and another three hundred pounds. Do you think it is reasonable that we should believe you instead of such great, educated and beneficed men?"

"My lady, I am translating a little book by the great scholar Erasmus. With your permission, I would like to present you with a copy of my translation. If you read it, you may think differently."

William gave Sir John and Lady Ann the copy, and they immediately began to study Erasmus' little book.

Sir John read aloud to his wife: "*Since faith is really the sole approach to Christ, the first rule should be that you understand as clearly as possible about Him and about the Holy Scripture handed down by His spirit and that you not entertain belief only by lip service... but let it permeate your whole being, let it be deeply and immovably fixed until there is not even an iota contained in Scripture that does not pertain to your spiritual well-being.*"

Lady Ann nodded attentively. "These words agree with William's advice. He would have us learn from the Scripture."

Sir John read on. "*Maintain your confidence that nothing you hear with your own ears or see with your own eyes or grasp in your own hands is so true, nothing is so certain and unquestionable as that which you read in the Scripture.*"

Once the Walshes read Erasmus' book, they did not invite the clergymen to dinner as frequently as they had in the past. The clergy blamed William.

As William preached in the country, crowds gathered to hear him. He realized that the need for the Scripture in English was critical. The people barely knew the Bible and their teachers were as ignorant as they were. In the evenings William began to translate the Holy Scripture into English from the Greek New Testament of Erasmus.

By Christmas he had prepared the second chapter of the Gospel of Saint Luke. He read to the people who gathered to hear him preach:

"And there were in the same region shepherds abiding in the field and watching their flock by night. And lo: the angel of the Lord stood hard by them, and the brightness of the Lord shone round about them, and they were sore afraid. But the angel said unto them: Be not afraid. For behold, I bring you tidings of great joy that shall come to all the people: for unto you is born this day in the city of David, a savior which is Christ the Lord."

William looked into the eyes of the men and women listening hungrily to the Scripture. Many of them were shepherds like these first men who heard the good news. They, too, needed these tidings of great joy. He explained how Jesus came as our savior to save us from our sins.

A sigh ran through the crowd. "A savior," someone murmured in wonder. William knew that his life work had begun.

Early one morning Edward came to see William. When William saw the worry in his eyes, he quickly left his students to meet with his brother.

"William, I was at the ale house yesterday and there was a group of our clerics. They spoke angrily of you and said that you were preaching heresy."

William laughed. "I'm too small a flea, Edward. They don't really care about me."

"But they care about the things you are saying. Words have a life of their own. Beware, lest you speak words that are easily misunderstood."

"My words are understood quite well. I am only speaking the truth, and these men know the Scripture supports my words."

Edward spoke firmly. "The priests have gone secretly to the chancellor and accused you of heresy. It is no longer safe for you here."

"I will not run away," said William.

Edward frowned. "If that is your decision, there will be a sitting of the bishop's chancellor, and he has ordered you to appear before him. The priests will be there as well." He clasped William's hand. "I pray God will help you."

William resorted to his Scripture as he prepared to testify before the chancellor. In the book of Romans he translated: "For I am not ashamed of the gospel of Christ… For by it the righteousness which cometh of God, is opened, from faith to faith. As it is written: The just shall live by faith." William pondered that word "faith." He prayed heartily that God would give him strength of faith to stand fast in the truth of the Bible.

The chancellor was a grim-faced man named Dr. Parker. The trial before him wore long into the afternoon. One after another, the local clergymen presented their tirades against William. One priest complained that he found William teaching salvation by faith alone. Another accused him of being a disrespectful wretch. A third scholar, whom William had never met, testified that William's doctrines dangerously resembled the heresies of Martin Luther, a name he spit out with disgust.

The chancellor listened impatiently to the lengthy charges. "We have heard enough to condemn this man," he declared.

William motioned to

speak, but the chancellor would not recognize him. "I have information brought to me secretly of even worse charges than we have heard today. William Tyndale is guilty of teaching heresy and drawing innocent people away from the church. He is disrespectful and unruly. He will not submit to authority, but boasts that he knows more than the priests. He has been heard to defy the Pope and all his laws. This is heresy!"

As he spoke, the chancellor's voice grew louder. He turned upon William and pounded the table for emphasis. "If you do not change your ways, I will personally see that you are brought to punishment. Nowhere will be safe. Flee immorality," he bellowed. "Flee!"

William blanched under the chancellor's railing words. He expected a closely reasoned trial, but nothing like these threats. Would they allow him to leave the trial as a free man?

The chancellor, spent from his loud oratory, resumed his seat. He continued to watch William with glittering eyes.

William rose slowly to his feet. In all the drama of the chancellor's scolding, he realized that the man had no evidence that he had misused his ordination. He was not a chaplain under the authority of the chancellor. Since he worked for Sir John, he was free to teach and preach. In his defense, William said simply, "I am content that you send me where you will into any county within England, as long as you bind me to nothing, but to teach children and preach."

Perhaps the mild words turned the chancellor's anger, or perhaps he saw the justice that William was not under his authority. At the end of the trial William was permitted to return to his home.

Sir John was relieved to see him again. "My lady and I

have spent this day praying for your safety," he told William.

When he heard all that had happened, his forehead creased with worry. "I'm not sure how much longer I can keep you safe here. But perhaps I can help you find one who will support you. You told me once that you studied under Dr. William Latimer. He was a chancellor to a bishop. Perhaps if you opened your mind to him upon these questions of Scripture, he could counsel you."

The next week William sought out his old professor. They had much to discuss since the printing of the Greek New Testament and the new books by Erasmus.

Professor Latimer had changed since William saw him last. He still wore his woolen neck warmer, but his hair had turned completely white, and he walked slowly with a stoop. "I fear for my countrymen," he explained to William. "The priests of this country are unlearned, and the people desperately need the Scripture. I have been an officer of the Pope, but I have given it up."

"Sir John hoped you might be able to help me," said William.

The older man bowed his head, then he fell silent. After a moment he continued. "Perhaps you should seek someone who would sponsor a translation of the Bible in English. I have a friend from my university days. His name is Cuthbert Tunstall."

"I know his name. He helped Erasmus with his Greek New Testament," said William.

"Aye, he is very knowledgeable. He is also bishop of London. He would be in the position to protect someone who wanted to translate the Scripture."

William thanked his old friend warmly. As he was about to depart, Latimer held up his hand. "Beware what you say, William. It could cost you your life."

When William returned to Little Sodbury Manor, he reported his conversation to Sir John. "I'm afraid that you would only incur trouble by keeping me," he said. "I would be sorry for that."

"You have my good will to depart," said Sir John. "I only regret that we will miss your conversation at the dinner table."

The next morning William left for London. As he reached the top of Nibley Knoll, he looked back for a last look over the countryside. Sheep grazed in the green fields that spread like a soft blanket on the hills. In the distance the eastern spur of the Welsh mountains made a blue line that melted into the sky.

William turned and followed the road that would lead him to London. As he trudged along the road, he reflected on Erasmus' words in *The Handbook of the Christian Knight*:

> "Let your first principle be, then, to have no doubt at all about God's promises; and the next, to enter upon the way of spiritual health, not slowly or timorously, but resolutely, wholeheartedly, with a confident and --if I may use the expression-- pugnacious spirit, ready to expend either your goods or your life for Christ."

Chapter 9

Deeds are the fruit of love; and love is the fruit of faith.
–William Tyndale

London

As he crossed London Bridge, William marveled at the dozens of narrow shops and houses squeezed along the edges. The Thames River boomed against the pilings and almost drowned the sound of townsmen hawking their wares.

William found lodging with a wool merchant who was a friend of his brother. The merchant lived above his shop and rented William a closet. Every morning William awoke to the sound of church bells. From St. Paul's to St. Dunstans the bells pealed merrily each hour and never at the same time. It meant that each hour was accompanied by a cacophony of bells that lasted several minutes.

William soon learned his way around London. There was a lady who sold fresh bread at the corner, and farther on was a fishmonger. He saw the Tower of London, which was built by William the Conqueror over four hundred years ago. Across town he found book stalls. William struck up a friendship with a bookseller, who secretly sold pamphlets by Martin Luther.

London

William also renewed many friendships with fellow students from Oxford and Cambridge including John Frith and Thomas Bilney. They were interested to learn of his work in translating the Greek New Testament into English. John was now a priest and Thomas was a professor of canon law. One evening they met in the backroom of the bookseller friend to discuss Scripture.

"The more I work on this translation, the more I realize that the Greek tongue agrees more with the English than with the Latin," William said.

John gave a satisfied sigh, and sat back in his chair, ready for a long talk. "Show me," he said.

William opened the Greek New Testament. "Look at the Greek word-play here in Romans 13. I have translated it 'the powers that be,' but if you wanted to express the same idea in Latin you would have something like 'the existing authorities' or some other complicated phrase.

Latin does not have the same flexibility as Greek and English."

"So you would not agree with those who say the Scripture cannot be translated into English because the language is too rude?" asked Thomas.

"No. Look at the Greek of the New Testament. It was the language of the common people and was meant to be understood by them. I want to write for the common people as well!"

William was invited to preach at St. Dunstan's Church in London. He preached there as he had done in Gloucestershire. He would translate the Holy Scripture into English as he preached so that the people could understand it plainly.

"Romans in the third chapter teaches us: a man is justified by faith without the deeds of the law," William preached. "Do we then destroy the law through faith? Paul says: God forbid. But we rather maintain the law because God gives us the power to love it and to keep it."

Many wizened faces in the crowd would nod as he spoke. He wondered if they remembered Scripture that had been passed by word of mouth from the days of Wycliffe, just as his grandmother had taught him.

On Maundy Thursday the king made his annual distribution to the poor. This was called the Royal Maundy and was based on the commandment or *mandatum* of Jesus that "you love one another." In great pomp, the king gave packets of clothing and little bags of money to the poor people who were brought in for the ceremony.

William turned a corner in time to see the end of the royal procession. A long line of retainers and squires thronged the narrow street and waved their pikes threateningly at any who dared approach. "That's Cardinal Wolsey's train in the middle," an old man said hoarsely.

"They say he is richer than the king."

William studied the stout man wearing red velvet robes and the cardinal's cap. How could he be a man of the church and yet withhold the Scripture from the people?

The next day William went with a letter from Sir John Walsh to visit Sir Henry Guildford. Sir Henry was Master of the Horse and controller of the Royal Household. He was a lively courtier and close friend to the king. There was a story that soon after Henry VIII married Queen Catherine, Sir Henry staged the arrival of Robin Hood and his Merry Men in the Queen's bedchamber. To her surprise, Robin Hood was the king. For this and other pranks, Sir Henry remained an active companion to the king.

William brought him his translation of a complicated oration by Isocrates. Isocrates was the founder of a school of rhetoric in Athens in the fourth century BC, and his orations were considered some of the finest examples of rhetoric in classical literature. William hoped to show his ability as a scholar and translator.

Sir Henry admired his translation. "My professor at Oxford praised Isocrates because he taught rhetoric should be used only for the highest goals."

William was delighted to find a fellow scholar. "Isocrates wrote that the art of speech would enlarge the mind and produce wisdom and virtue." One idea led to another and soon William found himself asking Sir Henry to speak to the bishop on his behalf.

The courtier was glad to help. He also urged William to write a letter and take it to the bishop at his home, the London House.

The London House was a large palace near Old St. Paul's Cathedral. William waited patiently as a flurry of officials and secretaries rushed past him. Sir Henry had warned him that the bishop would be too busy to see him personally. Parliament had been called for the first time in eight years, and the bishop was constantly occupied with the affairs of state. He had even addressed Parliament at its opening.

At the London House, William recognized a friend from college, William Hebilthwayte, who now served as one of the secretaries to the bishop. He asked his friend to deliver the letter. He left the palace full of hope that he would soon find a patron to support his translation work.

William waited anxiously for news from the bishop. He kept himself busy translating the New Testament from the Greek. As William studied, he found many differences between the original Greek and the Latin translation that was still used in the church.

William found that the Greek word *metanoeo* literally meant *repent*, but the Latin version translated it as *agere penitenciam,* which meant "to do penance." Penance had come to be a ritual that involved saying a certain number of prayers. In order to receive forgiveness, people had to confess to a priest, who would tell them how many prayers to say. From William's study of the Scripture, he realized it was God who forgave sinners, not the priests with their rituals of penance.

As William continued to preach at St. Dunstan's Church, word spread of his clear sermons. Soon the church was crowded. After one sermon, William met a man who introduced himself as Sir Humphrey Monmouth. He had made a successful business in the cloth industry. He was also an alderman of London.

Sir Humphrey asked William if his family was connected with the cloth trade and discovered that it was indeed the same Tyndale family. The two men enjoyed a pleasant hour discussing Gloucestershire. When Sir Humphrey asked William if he had a position in London,

William told him that he hoped to be employed by Bishop Tunstall.

"Indeed, that is a fine position for a Gloucestershire lad," said Sir Humphrey. Before he left, he gave William his address. "If you would like to be a chaplain in my house, come to this address."

At last the bishop's answer came. As William waited in the chilly evening outside of the bishop's palace, a secretary came with the message. "His Eminence is sorry, but he has chaplains enough. He advises you to seek employment in London where there are plenty of jobs for good scholars."

William thanked the secretary and began the long walk back to his lodging. He could hardly believe the message he received. He turned it over and over in his mind, as though it were a coin with a strange inscription. The secretary said that the bishop had chaplains enough. *But I was not applying to be simply a chaplain*, thought William.

Surely, the bishop, who had helped Erasmus with the Greek New Testament, would support the translation of the Bible into English. Yet the answer was "no." A sharp wind blew up from the Thames River and William pulled his thin coat tighter around him. He had hoped to find the wind of change blowing in London, but he was mistaken.

The next day William awoke early and went to see Sir Humphrey Monmouth. Monmouth remembered the enthusiastic young preacher and gladly hired him as his chaplain. He arranged for William to live at his house.

William found a sympathetic friend in Sir Humphrey. He encouraged William to translate the Scripture, and even had his secretary make copies of William's sermons. When William gave him a copy of Erasmus' *Enchiridion* in English, Monmouth asked his secretary to make a copy which he set on a table for his friends to peruse. The Abbess of Dennye and several other friends asked for copies of their own, which the secretary obligingly made.

Sir Humphrey also owned several other books in English by Martin Luther which he left in plain sight for everyone to read. He delighted to share these books with his guests, but William was concerned. Erasmus was honored in England, but the name of Luther could brand a person as a heretic.

"You might get in trouble for owning these books," William warned him.

"But no one, neither priest, nor friar, nor any layman has found great fault in them," replied Sir Humphrey. "The mischief we see in the church is the result of hiding the Scripture from the peoples' eyes."

William warmed to this idea. "I would do everything in my power to bring the plain Word of God to my countrymen. Once they have the Scripture, no enemy of the truth could snatch that away from them."

Sir Humphrey nodded thoughtfully. "How much of the Scripture have you translated?"

"Almost the entire New Testament, though it still needs work," said William.

Sir Humphrey stood near the table with his copies of Erasmus and Luther. He placed his hand reverently on the top-most book. "The time has come for you to go to the continent so that your translation can be published," he said. "The Holy Scripture must come to our people."

Wittenberg, about 1524

Chapter 10

And lo, I am with you always, even until the end of the world.
–Matthew 28:20 as translated by William Tyndale

Hebrew Studies

In April 1524, when Gloucestershire was full of wood anemones with their delicate white flowers and lacy leaves, William journeyed to Germany to find a way to print his translation of the New Testament.

He had another ambitious goal in mind. Professor Latimer once told William that the dark places in the Old Testament could not be understood unless one was versed in the Hebrew tongue and had the means of consulting Hebrew commentaries. Though Greek had come to England, none of the colleges taught the Hebrew language. William hoped to learn Hebrew at a German university.

A friend from the German community in London recommended that William stay with the von Emmersons of Hamburg. They offered to help William on his way to the

University of Wittenberg where he would study Hebrew. Their son, Matthias von Emmerson, was also preparing to go to the university and the two young men became fast friends.

In England, the persecution of Lutherans was growing worse, and the von Emmersons advised William to use a pseudonym. William reversed the syllables in his name and became "Daltin" instead of Tyndale. Thus, William Daltin lived with Matthias von Emerson for nine months at the university.

Martin Luther

In Wittenberg William met Martin Luther, whose writings he had studied at the White Horse Inn. Luther invited William and Matthias to join the students who frequently ate dinner with him in his home.

Luther regaled the students with the story of how he came to translate the New Testament into German. "I was travelling home from the Diet of Worms when suddenly I was surrounded by horsemen. They took me to a remote castle, and I thought this must surely be the end."

"How did you escape?" said Matthias.

"I didn't." Luther laughed heartily. "My kidnapper was a friend of the gospel--the Elector of Saxony, himself!"

"He was the founder of our university," said one student proudly.

"Aye, and he hid me in his castle when I was in danger of being burned at the stake. My refuge became a good place to study, and I used the time to translate the New

Testament into German."

"How long did it take?" asked William.

"I made good progress because there were no other distractions, so I finished in one year," Luther said.

A single year! William was impressed with such skill and dedication.

William also made the acquaintance of Melanchthon, one of the finest Greek scholars in Europe. William enjoyed talking with him about translation.

"The New Testament was written in the everyday language of the people," Melanchthon told him. "You should translate it into the best everyday English that you can. And remember that the first Christians were Hebrew. The Scripture spoke in Greek of concepts that were very Jewish, for example *burnt offerings* and *sacrifices for sin*."

William also met Andreas Osiander who often visited Wittenberg. Luther said that he was the best Hebrew scholar of their day. Along with several other scholars, he advised Luther in his Hebrew translation. Luther called this group "his Sanhedrin."

Luther published his German translation of the first five books of the Old Testament and William purchased a copy. It was the first published Scripture of the Old Testament translated from Hebrew to any language of that day. Luther continued to translate the rest of the Old Testament with the help of his Sanhedrin.

"I only learned Hebrew later," Luther told the students around his dinner table. "I bought a copy of Reuchlin's *De rudimentis* when it came out in 1507, but I did not have a teacher and the first six years were slow. I found that studying the Psalms helped the most."

William made rapid progress in his Hebrew studies, and showed his early work to Matthias. "I am finding that Hebrew translates into English beautifully."

"What do you mean?" asked Matthias, who knew only a little English.

"In the Hebrew the future tense is often the same as the imperative in the passive voice. It's the same in the English language! If you say 'you shall obey my commands' it is the same as 'be obedient to my commands.' I am able to translate quite literally into English."

Matthias shook his head. "Your English grammar is too much for me."

William enthusiastically rifled through his pages. "Here is another example," he said. "Look how English captures the way that Hebrew poetry is written with parallel phrases. 'He was wounded for our transgression, and bruised for our iniquities.'"

Matthias studied the passage. "It does make nice poetry in English," he conceded.

When William returned to the von Emmerson home in Hamburg, he found money waiting for him--sent by his faithful friend, Sir Humphrey Monmouth.

Chapter 11

I have here translated (brethren and sisters most dear and tenderly beloved in Christ) the new Testament for your spiritual edifying, consolation and solace.
-- William Tyndale in the Prologue to the first New Testament in English, 1525

Printing

During the summer of 1525, William travelled to Cologne. He watched the shore slip by, as the Rhine wound past bustling cities and stone castles that stood high above the waterway. The fourth day the Rhine passed through a rocky gorge.

William peered into the depths of the greenish water and remembered the tales the old shepherd, Franz, had told him of a golden ring guarded by Rhine maidens. According to Franz, the ring would give power over the world. William reflected how God's word was more powerful than any fairy tale ring. If only its power could be unlocked for his countrymen in England.

William began printing the English New Testament at Cologne at the printing house of Peter Quentell. The printer, with his broad shoulders and thick beard, towered over William.

"I can make your New Testament look as magnificent as Luther's Bible," Peter said. "We will fill the first page with a woodcut and put large illuminations at the beginning of each chapter."

Cologne

"Wait, my friend, we must print this book smaller. It must fit in a pocket, because there are men in England who would not smile on the Bible being read or carried in plain view," said William.

"We can make it small enough to fit in a gentleman's pocket, too," Peter assured him.

One curious thing about Peter Quentell was that he followed Luther's ideas about the superiority of the gospels and the letters by Peter, John and Paul. These books were carefully numbered. Hebrews, James, Jude, and Revelation, however, were not numbered and were printed separately. William puzzled over Peter's behavior.

"How can you treat the last four books differently?" he asked Peter. "The Bible-- even the hard places-- must be taken as a whole, so that it can interpret itself."

Peter shrugged. "Our printing house has been printing Bibles since before you were born. The complete Dutch Bible was printed here almost fifty years ago."

William worked long hours at the print shop, but his progress was slow. He realized that he needed someone to help him check the proofs for accuracy.

One afternoon a young man entered the Quentell printing house. He wore a friar's habit and carried a thin bag over his shoulder.

"I am seeking William Tyndale," he announced.

Peter strode forward, his large frame blocking the presses from view. "Why do you seek him?" he asked in his rumbling voice.

The friar shrank back against the doorframe. "A friend of Master Tyndale recommended that I seek employment with him."

"And why would you want such employment?" said Peter.

"I used to be a friar, but now I believe the best way I can serve the Lord is in printing the Bible."

Peter's face was still wary, but William himself stepped around him. "Read this and tell me what you think."

The friar took up the piece of paper and read aloud: "Christ bringeth God. Where Christ is, there is God: and where Christ is not, there is not God."

"Do you believe this?" asked William.

"Aye, I do," he said.

"Do you have the patience to examine a proof and compare every word to the original manuscript?"

"I know I do!"

"And are you willing to work long hours with small pay?"

The friar swung his meager pack and grinned. "I have all I need right here."

"Then allow me to introduce myself. I am William Tyndale and I would be glad to employ your services."

"William Roye, at your service."

Roye proved to be a great help. As the printer made progress on the Gospel of Matthew, Roye checked stacks of proofs. In addition to the Scripture, there were cross references to other verses in the inside margins and commentary in the outside margins.

The gospel of Matthew began with a woodcut of an angel holding an ink pot for the apostle Matthew to dip his pen. At each chapter division the printer put in large illuminations. One day Roye held up one of the pages. "This printing is beautiful," he told William. "Surely, nothing like this could have been printed in England with the presses we have there."

William smiled but barely looked up. He was sitting in the midst of a dozen books open to various passages, which he checked and re-checked. He used both editions of Luther's New Testament because the marginal notes were helpful. In addition to translating many of Luther's comments, he was adding his own notes.

He dipped his pen in the ink and wrote a note on the meaning of the name given to Jesus: "*Jesus* is as much to say as a *saver*, for he only saveth all men from their sins by his mercies without their deserving."

The next note he needed to write was about Simon Peter. "Roye, why do you think our Lord gave Simon a new name?"

Roye looked puzzled. "I never thought about it before."

"Peter in the Greek signifies a rock in English," said William. "Simon's confession that Jesus is the Christ is like a rock of the gospel."

"Do you think people will understand the word *gospel*?" said Roye.

William pulled out a piece of parchment. "Here is what I have written in the prologue. See if you think this is clear."

Roye read: "*Evangelion (that we call the gospel) is a Greek word and signifieth good, merry, glad and joyful tidings, that maketh a man's heart glad, and maketh him sing, dance, and leap for joy.*" He skipped down the page. "I like this part: *Yet are we full of the natural poison, our nature is to do sin, as is the nature of a serpent to sting.* I think our readers cannot fail to understand that point!"

"Here is the Bible verse I want to use at the end of the prologue. I have just revised my translation. I think it will encourage our brothers and sisters."

Roye took the page and read: "*Who shall separate us from the love that God loveth us withal? Shall tribulation? Anguish? Persecution? Shall hunger? Nakedness? Shall a sword? Nay, I am sure that neither death, nor life, neither angel, neither rule, nor power, neither present things, nor things to come, neither high nor low, neither any other creature is able to separate us from the love of God which is in Christ Jesus our Lord.*"

While William worked in Cologne, he heard from his friend, John Frith. He had been asked by Cardinal Wolsey to teach at his new college at Oxford. William considered John to be one of the most talented scholars he had ever met. "He will make the new college a bright light among the many colleges at Oxford," he predicted.

A scholar named John Dobneck was printing several large volumes at Peter Quentell's shop. He called himself 'Cochlaeus' and had published a tract defending the book that Henry VIII had written against Luther. He was also a spy to the English court on the activities of the heretical Protestants.

Dobneck was suspicious of the two Englishmen whom he frequently met at the press. One evening he invited the print shop workers to join him at a tavern. When they were drunk, he asked them about the Englishmen. They boasted

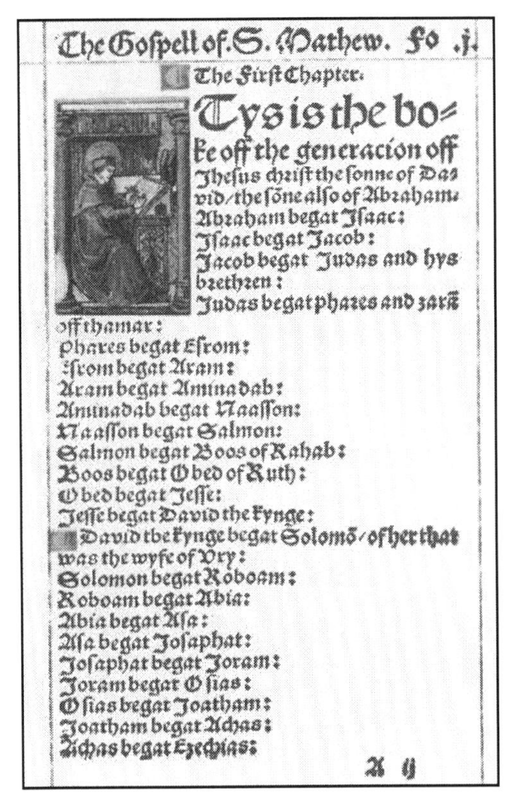
The Gospell of. S. Mathew. Fo .j.

The First Chapter.

Tys is the booke off the generacion off Jhesus christ the sonne of David/the sone also of Abraham.
Abraham begat Isaac:
Isaac begat Jacob:
Jacob begat Judas and hys brethren:
Judas begat phares and zaram off thamar:
Phares begat Esrom:
Esrom begat Aram:
Aram begat Aminadab:
Aminadab begat Naasson:
Naasson begat Salmon:
Salmon begat Boos of Rahab:
Boos begat Obed of Ruth:
Obed begat Jesse:
Jesse begat David the kynge:
David the kynge begat Solomo/of her that was the wyfe of Vry:
Solomon begat Roboam:
Roboam begat Abia:
Abia begat Asa:
Asa begat Josaphat:
Josaphat begat Joram:
Joram begat Osias:
Osias begat Joatham:
Joatham begat Achas:
Achas begat Ezechias:

A ij

The first page of the Gospel of Matthew with a large illumination

that the Englishmen were printing three thousand New Testaments in the English language and soon all of England would be Lutheran.

Dobneck immediately reported this to a senator of Cologne who was known to sympathize with King Henry VIII. The senator convinced the senate to prohibit the printers and sent soldiers to impound the printed sheets.

Roye burst into the printshop with the news. "We have been discovered!"

William jumped up and swept his books into a satchel. Peter yelled to his men to take down the drying pages, and he lifted the great sheaf of printed pages onto a cart that stood at the back door.

"Quickly," he urged William. "They will not stop at taking the Bibles if you are here as well."

William and Roye leaped onto the back of the cart and pulled a great canvas over themselves. As the cart rumbled away, the stamp of booted feet and a pounding on the printshop door could be heard.

That morning a merchant ship left the port for Worms. Hidden in the hold were William Tyndale, his assistant and the first twenty-two chapters of the gospel of Matthew.

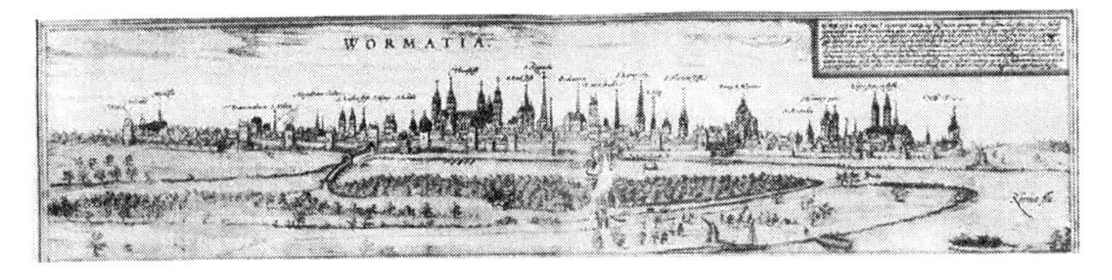

The city of Worms, Germany

Chapter 12

When the gospel is preached to us, he (God) openeth our hearts, and giveth us grace to believe and putteth the spirit of Christ in us, and we know him as our father most merciful, and consent to the law, and love it inwardly in our heart, and desire to fulfill it, and sorrow because we cannot... the blood of Christ hath obtained all things for us of God.

-- William Tyndale in the prologue to the 1525 New Testament in English.

The Smuggler's Trade

Worms was a smaller city, but had a proud history of hosting assemblies called "diets" in its beautiful cathedral. Only five years earlier the Diet at Worms had called Martin Luther to account for his beliefs. He stood before the glittering assembly of the highest church and political officials and said, "Here I stand; I can do no other. God help me. Amen."

In Worms William found a printer named Peter Shoeffer, who printed German Bibles. He whistled when William told him that he wanted to print six thousand English New Testaments.

"My father's largest order was two thousand. Even the great Martin Luther's first German New Testament was only four thousand," said the printer. "I would be risking good paper and ink, not to mention the wages of my men."

"I have money from England to pay for paper and ink. When the books sell I can pay you the rest."

The printer hesitated, but William added, "Martin Luther has printed a great deal more since then, and it was his advice to begin with a larger number. The need is great."

"The need is great, you say?" The printer slapped the table with his strong hand. "Then we will do it!"

William began anew to publish the New Testament. Roye helped him to proof and compare the texts. For this edition he did not include his prologue or notes in the margins. He did not put his name on the title page because of Christ's instruction to do 'good deeds secretly and to be content with the conscience of well doing.'

William sent the unbound manuscripts that he saved from his first printing into England. In London they were bound and sold in bookshops around the city. The books contained only the first twenty-two chapters of Matthew and the prologue, but they sold quickly. The prologue itself caused quite a stir with the theme that "whoever flieth to Christ, can neither hear nor receive of God any other thing save mercy." With the money from these sales, William was able to pay for food and lodging in Worms.

One afternoon William worked in the print shop to proof pages of the New Testament. The pale light filtered through the dusty windows, and the pages drying on lines above his head cast shifting shadows on the paper before him. Carefully William checked each word of the fifth chapter of Romans. He was not aware that he spoke aloud as he read: "Because therefore that we are justified by faith, we are at peace with God through our lord Jesus Christ."

"Peace with God?" queried a small voice at his shoulder. William looked up into the lively eyes of the printer's son.

William smiled. "Peace with God means that our sins are no longer held against us."

"What about fasting and alms? My grandmother says that is how we make peace with God."

William thought carefully before he answered. "The blood of Jesus is stronger than all the sins and wickedness of the whole world. When we have faith in Jesus, we are born anew. Without Jesus, we will perish even though we have a thousand holy candles about us and a hundred tons of holy water."

Before William could speak further the printer called for his son. William reflected on their conversation and added a few notes to the epilogue he was preparing:

> Give diligence Reader (I exhort thee) that thou come with a pure mind, and as the Scripture saith with a single eye, unto the words of health, and of eternal life: by the which (if we repent and believe them) we are born anew, created afresh, and enjoy the fruits of the blood of Christ.

Though Roye was a help in checking proofs, William began to worry about his character. He seemed to relish fighting the church officials more than getting the Holy Scripture into the hands of the people. He actually enjoyed reading a book that Sir Thomas More had written (in Latin) against Luther. It was full of name-calling and degrading images that were embarrassing to read. Roye, however, chuckled to himself as he read. "Thomas More writes that Luther 'would cast into his mouth the dung which other men would spit out into a basin.'"

William rubbed his eyes which burned from checking the cramped letters of the proof. "Master Roye, please do not read any further. I can assure you that it goes on like this for pages and pages."

Roye put his thumb in the book to hold his place. "Let him throw filth! We can throw it right back."

William shook his head. "Translating the Holy Scripture is a high calling," he said sternly. "We cannot stoop to Sir Thomas' mud-slinging."

Roye returned to his proof work, but soon stopped William again. "Listen to this from II Corinthians. It sounds like the problem with the Roman Church." Roye grinned as he read: "*But their minds were blinded. For until this day remaineth the same covering untaken away in the old testament when they read it, which in Christ is put away*. The Roman Church is blind too, though I can't say that they are even reading the Old Testament!"

William looked up from the page before him. "Master Roye, be careful of becoming overly proud. That same passage in II Corinthians also says *But we have this treasure in earthen vessels that the excellent power of it might appear to be of God and not of us*. Remember that Jesus said that love is the end and the fulfilling of all laws."

At last the first English New Testament was ready for shipment. Among the English merchants William had several friends who helped smuggle the Bibles. Their workmen picked up wrapped packages from the print shop and distributed them through a maze of underground chambers where they were packed among bales of merchandise. The merchants shipped the hidden New Testaments across the English Channel and up the Thames River to the docks of the Steelyard.

The Steelyard was a German community just below London Bridge. Many of the workers were Christians whose lives had been changed through the work of Martin Luther. They worked by candlelight to transfer the smuggled Bibles to carts which made deliveries in great secrecy around London.

Sir Henry Monmouth, whose vast business reached even remote corners of England, helped the contraband goods on their way. In less than a month the English New Testaments spread over the south and eastern regions of England.

Sir Humphrey entrusted the proceeds from the shipment to Hans Collenbeke, who lived in the Steelyard and was returning to Germany. Hans found William in the print shop.

"Sir Humphrey bids you God's grace," he said as he slipped a bulging envelope to William. "I am to tell you that your merchandise sold out in a single week."

"How are your people faring?" asked William.

Hans grimaced. "Cardinal Wolsey—the one we call Wolfsee—sent officers to raid the Steelyard and burn all the German New Testaments and Lutheran tracts that they could find. There's a rumor that Bishop Tunstall plans to make a great show of burning the English New Testament, too."

William was saddened by the news. Tunstall had helped Erasmus with the Greek New Testament. He knew better than anyone that the translation was sound. William could understand if he destroyed a booklet by a human author, but to burn the Word of God! How could it be?

Roye seemed to swell in importance as he heard the news. "That's why someone needs to show the world that Cardinal Wolsey is a scoundrel and Bishop Tunstall is a hypocrite!"

"Master Roye, do you really think that would help our cause? It would only fuel their fires more," said William.

A few days later, Roye left abruptly. He went to Strasbourg and was soon publishing books of his own. William was concerned about Roye's style. He taunted the church leaders. He also tried to justify his writing by boasting of his work on the New Testament.

In the spring a friar named Jerome Barlow visited from England. He told William that he planned to join Roye to help with his work.

William warned him of Roye's growing boldness. "Beware of him, and walk quietly and with all patience," he told the young man. "Violent speech against the English authorities will only hurt the acceptance of the Bible in English. The authority of the Word of God is at stake."

Unfortunately, when Jerome joined William Roye in Strasbourg, Roye convinced him to write poems attacking Cardinal Wolsey. They were published as a book entitled "Rede Me and Be Not Wroth." The title page showed a picture of Cardinal Wolsey with his hat painted red surrounded by axes dripping with red blood.

When a friend brought a copy to William, he was distressed. He read the light-hearted rhymes that held bitter mocking such as:

> He declared there in his furiousness
> That he found errors more and less
> Above three thousand in the translation.
> Howbeit when all came to pass
> I daresay unable he was
> Of one error to make probation.

"A man ought to rebuke wickedness with God's word and not with railing rhymes," William said.

He worried that such raillery would make it hard for those who were seeking the true gospel in England. His fears were proved true when he heard from Miles Coverdale.

Miles wrote that their faithful mentor, Friar Barnes, was on trial for heresy. Miles, versed in canon law, helped him prepare his defense, but the trial did not go well. After the trial Miles realized that he could not remain a monk. He renounced his orders and served as a secular priest, preaching in Essex, England.

cxix.

The Gospell off
Sancte Jhon.
The fyrst Chapter.

IN the begynnyng
was that worde/ ãd tha
worde was with god: and go
was thatt worde. The sam
was in the begynnynge wy
god. All thyngs were made
it/ and with out it/ was ma
noo thige/ that made was.
it was lyfe/ And lyfe was

Tyndale's 1525 English New Testament
First page of the Gospel of Saint John

Chapter 13

The sermons which thou readest in the Acts of the apostles, and all that the apostles preached, were no doubt preached in the mother tongue. Why then might they not be written in the mother tongue?

--William Tyndale, *The Obedience of a Christian Man*

The Pleasant Rain of the Gospel

While the New Testaments, hidden in bales of cloth, were making their way across the English Channel, William wrote a tract called *A compendious introduction, prologue or preface unto the epistle of Paul to the Romans.* It was based on Luther's prologue to Romans in the German New Testament. He expanded on Luther's theme to make the idea of justification by faith as clear as possible to his English readers:

> For how is it possible to do anything well in the sight of God, while we are yet in bondage and captivity under the devil, and the devil possesseth us altogether and holdeth our

> hearts, so that we cannot once consent unto the will of God.

"I like Luther's phrase 'the thunder of the Law,'" said Peter Schoeffer, the printer.

"Aye, but I would add *the pleasant rain of the gospel* that comes after it," countered William.

William dipped his pen in the ink. "I will add a short explanation of the Lord's Prayer to help people understand its meaning. It grieves me to see the terrible ignorance of the lay people who say the *pater noster* in the Latin tongue and do not even understand what they are saying."

Augustine Packington was a successful merchant and friend of William. With his broad shoulders and booming voice, he inspired confidence in everyone who did business with him. He met Bishop Tunstall in Antwerp and learned that the bishop wanted to buy the English New Testaments so that he could burn them.

Packington had an idea to turn the bishop's plan into a way to help William. He made the bishop an offer. "My lord! I can do more in this matter than most merchants that are here. If it be your lordship's pleasure, give me money to pay for them, and I will acquire every book of them that is printed and unsold."

The bishop eagerly agreed.

Packington went to William and told him that he had found someone who would pay cash for the rest of the New Testaments.

"Who is the merchant?" asked William.

"Cuthbert Tunstall, the Bishop of London," Packington said.

"What does he want with them?" asked William.

"He has a plan to burn them." Packington's tone was solemn, but his eyes twinkled with merriment.

William studied his friend's face for a moment. "Why would I want to sell?" he asked slowly.

Packington laughed. "Two benefits will come of this, William. You will get money to pay for this printing and the whole world will cry out upon the burning of God's word."

Packington arranged the sale, and when William received his money, he found that he not only had enough to pay Peter Shoeffer for the first printing, but enough left to print three times as many New Testaments, which were better proofed than the first printing.

When the bishop learned that there were more New Testaments than ever, he called Packington to him. "How can there be so many New Testaments abroad? You promised me that you would buy them all."

Packington answered, "I bought all that were to be had, but I perceive they have printed more since that time. I see it will never be better so long as they have paper and ink. You must buy the paper, too, if you want to be sure to stop them all."

The bishop said bitterly. "I see the joke is on me this time, but there will be an end to Tyndale's work."

One afternoon William was wrestling with the word *oligopistoi.* It was a Greek word that meant something like *O ye endued with little faith.* That was how William translated it in the first translation, but he knew there ought to be a better way. As he rolled words on his tongue, he tried *O ye of little faith.* That was it! He made a note in the margin and started on the next phrase.

"Master Tyndale, news of England!"

William looked up from the proofs to see young Tom, the secretary to one of the English merchants. His face was flushed from running and he was waving a letter in one hand.

"What is the news Tom?"

"My sister wrote to say your family sends you greetings. Your brother Edward has a second son and he has named him William."

"Another William Tyndale?"

"My sister bade me send you word of George Constantine. He was apprehended by the chancellor of England."

"Aye, I know the chancellor well," replied William. "He calls the English Bible heresy and would snuff out such work if he could."

"Tis the same," said Tom. "I am to tell you that George is safe, but that he was closely questioned by Sir Thomas More. He asked who provided the money for William Tyndale."

"And what did George tell him?" asked William.

Tom opened his eyes wide in mock seriousness. "He told him it was the bishop of London for he bestowed a great deal of money upon the New Testaments to burn them!"

William grinned. "It's true that the bishop's money has been our comfort."

Over the next few months the news from England grew worse. In November 1527 the chancellor began arresting people. Thomas Bilney and John Frith were two friends of William who were arrested and tortured. They were later released, but were ordered to stop preaching heresy.

William received a letter from his brother John. There was a campaign around London to find all the Lollards and Lutherans. The prisons were full. John had been arrested and interrogated for having letters from William. Though he was released, he worried that William was in danger.

As William carefully hid the letter, he prayed that the authorities would not learn about the money John was sending him.

William reflected that the children of Israel had the Old Testament in their own language. How could it be that those who lived 1500 years after the Messiah were not allowed the Scripture in their own tongue?

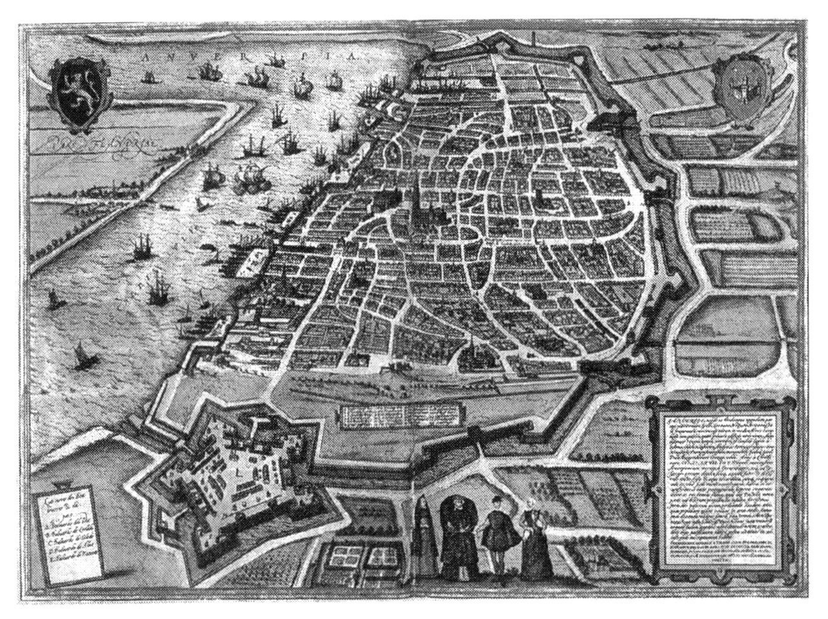

Antwerp

Chapter 14

"...and we are in eternal life already, and feel already in our hearts the sweetness thereof, and are overcome with the kindness of God and Christ and therefore love the will of God, and of love are ready to work freely, and not to obtain that which is given us freely and whereof we are heirs already."

--William Tyndale in *The Parable of the Wicked Mammon*

Thomas Hitton

The tulips were blossoming along the Schelde River as William held the first copy of his next book, *The Parable of the Wicked Mammon*. He now lived in Antwerp, a major port of the Low Countries. The city lay on a curve of the Schelde River where an estuary formed. From Antwerp, ships sailed the river fifty-five miles to the North Sea and on to trade with England.

William wandered the maze of streets until he reached the English House at a crossroads between the town center and the English Quay. The community of merchants in Antwerp were wealthy and powerful. They were known as the Merchant Adventurers from the days of Henry IV, when the crown of England had a monopoly on the wool trade. Since they could not trade in wool, some enterprising merchants chartered a company of adventurers who would trade the cloth made from the wool.

Antwerp

The Merchant Adverntures brought so much commerce to Antwerp that the city gave them a permanent house. It became known as the English House. Here in the safety of the English community, William found a place to finish his work.

In Antwerp over sixty printers flourished in a good trade of books exported to England. William's printer was Johannes Hoochstraten of Antwerp, but for *The Parable of the Wicked Mammon* the printer called himself "Hans Luft of Marburg."

The printer laughed. "It's safer that way. We also have a little fun. I've been Adam Anonymous of Basel and Peter Congeth of Parishe. Some printers give their location as Utopia!"

For the first time, William put his name on the book: "William Tyndale otherwise called Hychins." He knew that he must identify himself so that he could distinguish his work on the New Testament from the scurrilous booklets written by William Roye. The cause of the gospel required it.

In his new book, William again based his work on a booklet by Luther, but he added so much to it that it was five times as long as Luther's booklet. He began with his theme:

> That faith, the mother of all good works, justifieth us, before we can bring forth any good work: as the husband marrieth his wife before he can have any lawful children by her.

At the beginning of his book, William printed Jesus' parable from Luke 16 about the "wicked mammon." In this parable an unjust steward uses his master's wealth to make friends for himself before he loses his position.

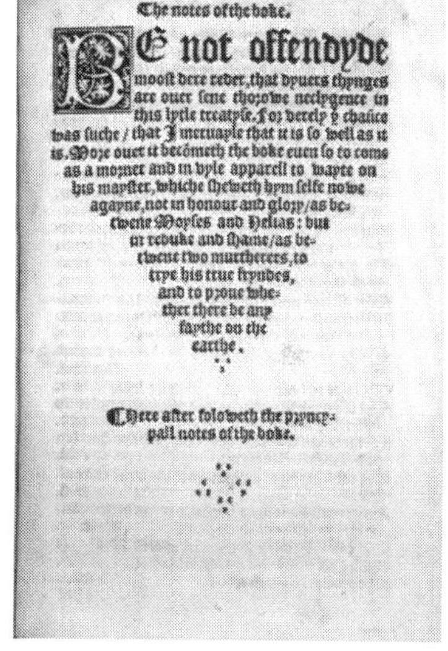

¶ The notes of the boke.

BE not offendyde moost dere reder, that dyuers thynges are ouer sene thorowe neclygence in this lytle treatyse. For verely ẏ chaūce was suche / that I meruayle that it is so well as it is. More ouer it becōmeth the boke euen so to come as a mourner and in vyle apparell to wayte on his mayster, whiche sheweth hym selfe nowe agayne, not in honour and glory / as betwene Moyses and Helias: but in rebuke and shame / as betwene two murtherers, to trye his true frendes, and to proue whether there be any faythe on the earthe.

¶ Here after foloweth the pryncypall notes of the boke.

William used dozens of Bible passages to show that not only does faith alone justify, but "true faith will always reveal itself in good works done freely and without thought of reward."

William kept in touch with Miles who was preaching in England. Miles wrote to him of Sir Humphrey Monmouth and how he was interrogated by Sir Thomas More and put in the prison of the Tower of London. The new bishop of London, Stokesley, accused him of reading heretical books, agreeing with Luther, helping Tyndale over the sea, and affirming that only faith justifies.

As the persecution in England intensified, Miles fled to the continent of Europe. William invited him to join him in his work.

William also had the help of a new friend from England named Thomas Hitton. Thomas was a slight young man with serious gray eyes. He wore a ragged brown coat that he claimed he could never part with because his sister made it for him. Like William and Miles, Thomas wanted to bring the gospel to England.

He read William's new book with pleasure. "This is beautifully written," he said. "I like how you explain that faith sets the soul at liberty to follow the will of God."

Miles added, "I was encouraged by the notion that there is nothing to exclude the simplest laymen from the upper reaches of the spiritual life."

"Aye, every man, whether a brewer, baker, tailor, merchant or farmer, can work as serving Christ himself," said William. "That is a life of devotion."

"You know that Cardinal Wolsey has found over twenty heresies in your *Parable of the Wicked Mammon,"* said Miles. "There is a rumor that he has asked that you be handed over as a heretic."

The rumor proved to be true. Though the authorities could not find Tyndale, they arrested an English merchant named Richard Herman in Antwerp. Herman had heretical books for sale, but he was not sent to England. The Regent of the Low Countries claimed that by law the trial must take place in his court. His judges would investigate and hold the trial in Antwerp. When the evidence from England was not sufficient, the Regent's court released Herman seven months later.

Meanwhile, William knew he would have to use more caution in smuggling books into England. The merchants helped him design clever hiding places for the contraband books. They had chests made with secret compartments. They wrapped books in bales of cloth or packed them in sacks of meal. They used a system of symbols and passwords to communicate. William moved lodgings frequently and introduced himself as William Daltin. Only his closest associates knew his true identity.

During the next five months William wrote another book called *The Obedience of a Christian Man*. His goal was to strengthen the faith of his readers, especially when they faced persecution. He wrote:

> Let it not make thee despair, neither yet discourage thee, O reader, that it is forbidden thee in pain of life and goods, or that it is made breaking of the king's peace, or treason unto his highness, to read the Word of thy soul's health;... for if God be on our side, what matter maketh it who be against us, be they bishops, cardinals, popes...

William wrote persuasively that the Bible should be available in English for all to read because it was the fountainhead of Christianity. It could be understood without the need for scholars to interpret and add "hidden meanings." He wrote:

> Thou shalt understand, therefore, that the Scripture hath but one sense which is the literal sense. And that literal sense is the root and ground of all, and the anchor that never faileth, whereunto if thou cleave thou canst never err or go out of the way.

The book itself was scarcely larger than a man's hand, and was smuggled quickly into England. In the 270 pages of the book, quotations from the Bible were on every page. William prayed that the gospel would reach many of his countrymen.

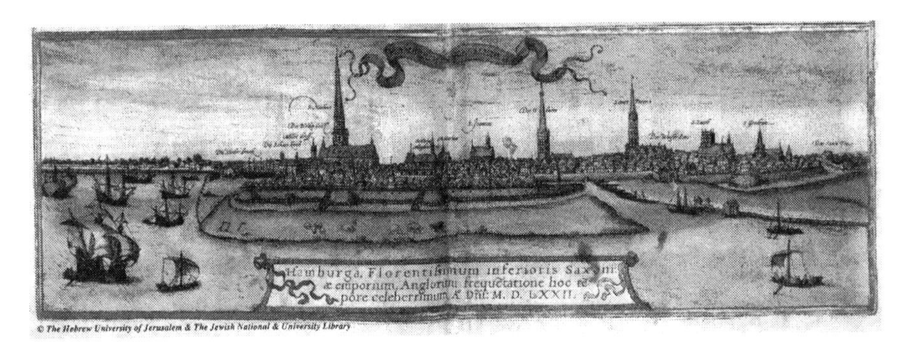

Hamburg, 1527

Chapter 15

"I call God to record against the day we shall appear before our Lord Jesus, that I never altered one syllable of God's Word against my conscience, nor would do this day, if all that is in earth, whether it be honor, pleasure, or riches, might be given me."

--William Tyndale in a letter to John Frith

Loss

William gathered his papers and looked with satisfaction at his growing pile of translation work. Soon the book of Deuteronomy would be finished. He had heard from a printer in Hamburg who would publish the work. William planned to journey there by boat.

The boat swayed gently under William's feet as he watched the banks of the Low Countries slip away. At last his plans for publishing the first five books of the Old Testament would be fulfilled. William brought not only the draft of his translation, but also all his books, the copies of the New Testament translation that he was always proofing, other papers and all his money.

As the day wore on, black clouds collected to the east. The captain studied the horizon with his spy glass. "It's not too late in the season for a squall."

Sailing ship

Even as he spoke the sky darkened and a stiff wind caught the sail. Slate-gray waves dashed against the ship. Within moments the storm struck.

"Passengers below," shouted the captain.

William staggered down the stairs and braced his shoulder against a pillar in the dark hold. The shriek of the wind mixed with the hoarse shouts of the men above decks. The ship tilted and William hurtled against something sharp. In the blackness William felt the warm trickle of blood on his forehead. *God bids us to trust in Him.* The simple truth was like an anchor as the frenzy around him grew. The dozen other passengers were scrambling to regain a hold as the ship lurched again. Some groaned. Others cried out in terror.

Despite his own fear, William felt a need to say something that would calm the passengers. "We must put ourselves in the Lord's hands," he shouted above the clamor. "Let us pray." With a steady voice that he did not know that he possessed, William began to pray. Psalms that he had studied sprang to his mind, and he spoke them in German since the passengers spoke this language. As the wind and sea dashed the ship from side to side, the hold of the ship grew quiet except for William's firm voice reciting Scripture after Scripture.

Suddenly there was a splintering crash and with a shudder the ship listed to the side. A sailor opened the hatch and frantically motioned for the passengers to follow him. "The ship is sinking!" he yelled above the storm. "The captain says you must come at once."

William groped for the large chest containing his books and money, but the sailor pulled him by the arm. "There's only room in the boat for people. We can't take anything with us."

William groaned inwardly, but the psalms he had so recently spoken to the other passengers gave him peace. *Rest assured that He will do what is best for us.* William left the books and papers and stumbled after the sailor to the waiting boat.

When William arrived in Hamburg, he began his work again. His greatest blessing was the help of Miles Coverdale who helped him begin again with Genesis. The men worked from Easter until December in the welcoming home of the van Emmersons. William considered Hamburg a safe city since it had recently reformed its church.

The work went well in Hamburg, but a great sweating sickness broke out in the town. At Christmas of 1529, William and Miles returned to Antwerp. There they heard the tragic news of Thomas Hitton, who was their companion when they were last in Antwerp.

Hitton had gone back to England to preach. He served as a priest in Maidstone but was arrested and cruelly tortured. After being examined by the archbishop, he was condemned as a heretic and burned alive before the door of his own parish church. The priests promised indulgences to commit sin for forty days to anyone who would carry fire wood for burning the heretic. William grieved deeply at the memory of Thomas Hitton with his serious gray eyes full of hope for the gospel.

William remembered the words of Erasmus. He warned that the Christian must always be prepared for battle.

William knew that he must pray for fresh resolve for the battle the Lord set before him.

Sir Thomas More

The newest attack appeared in the *Dialogue Concerning Heresies* written by Sir Thomas More. He was the Lord Chancellor of England and an avid opponent of Bible translation.

"I find it interesting that he is no longer writing in Latin," William mused. "Perhaps he is beginning to see the worth of writing in English."

Miles looked up from reading the book. "I marked the place where he wrote about you. He says that you were 'well known to be a man of right good living, studious and well learned in Scripture,' even though he does call you a heretic and says that there are so many faults in your New Testament that it wasn't worth fixing." Miles scanned the pages. "He also accuses you of having a wife! He says that's the only reason you say priests may marry."

"Sir Thomas More is up to his old tricks, I see."

Miles sighed. "When More wrote that there never was a heretic who wouldn't perjure himself to save his life, I thought of Thomas Hitton. He never denied the Lord Christ, though he was burned alive."

William bowed his head. "May we all die as well as that."

Chapter 16

"For... learning and comfort, is the fruit of the Scripture and the cause why it was written. And with such a purpose to read it, is the way to everlasting life, and to those joyful blessings that are promised unto all nations in the seed of Abraham, which seed is Jesus Christ our Lord, to whom be honour and praise for ever and unto God our Father through him. Amen."

--William Tyndale in the *Prologue to Genesis*

The Pentateuch

During the years that William lived in Antwerp, the city became the chief money market of Europe. Some people called it the *Venice of the North*. Besides a thriving economy built on ship-building and trade, Antwerp boasted the beautiful Gothic Cathedral of Notre Dame, which was over 400 feet high and the largest cathedral in the Low Countries.

A few blocks from the cathedral William met in the homes of the growing number of English exiles. Every Monday William visited this community to preach and encourage them. He read Scripture in English and shared some of his fresh revisions of the New Testament.

There were always improvements to make. This week

he was reading from the Sermon on the Mount. In his first translation he had written *blessed are the maintainers of peace*, but in his newest revision he translated: *blessed are the peacemakers*. *Peacemakers* was a single word like the Greek word: *eirenopoioi*, and made a neater translation.

His friends in the refugee community were charmed with the new word. "Peacemakers—that is what we are to be," exclaimed one man.

His wife added, "Even when we are far from our country we can pray for peace there."

From early morning to late at night, William worked to finish his translation of the five books of Moses. Miles helped him proof his work in preparation for printing.

As Miles completed his inspection of Genesis, he carefully smoothed the sheaf of pages. "This is amazing. I don't believe there is a single Hebrew scholar at any of the universities in England, and yet I'm holding in my hands pieces of the Hebrew Scripture translated directly into English!"

William tried to match the dignity of the Hebrew by using simple words and the rhythm of the English language. Where English did not have a word, he translated the word literally to coin words such as *mercyseat, scapegoat,* and *passover*, or he transliterated the Hebrew letters and brought the word into English, as in the case of *Jehovah*.

William made a list of new words with their meanings, which appeared at the beginning of the book. For the word *Jehovah,* the sacred name of God, William wrote:

> Jehovah is God's name, neither is any creature so called. And is as much to say as one that is of himself, and dependeth of nothing. Moreover as oft as thou seest LORD in great letters (except there be any error in

the printing) it is in Hebrew Jehovah, thou
that art or he that is.

At last the proofs were ready to publish. In Antwerp Hoochstraten's press worked far into the night printing the first five books of the Old Testament which comprised the Pentateuch.

In the book of Exodus the printer added eleven woodcuts. These illustrations showed things such as the ark of the covenant and other helpful pictures. Exodus, Leviticus, and Deuteronomy were printed in roman type which was lighter than the usual type used in Genesis. Genesis itself had only six marginal notes, unlike Martin Luther's Genesis which had seventy-two. The Scriptures were presented simply, yet William knew they would be powerful because they were the very words of God.

In the prologue to Exodus, William wrote: "Cleave unto the text and plain story and endeavour thyself to search out the meaning of all that is described thereon."

William held the printed book of the Pentateuch in his hands on the wintry evening of the seventeenth of January, 1530. He opened to the sixth chapter of Deuteronomy: "And thou shalt love the LORD thy God with all thine heart, with all thy soul and with all thy might." He prayed that God would use these English Old Testament books to stir up such love for the Lord.

As quickly as the books came off the press, they were smuggled into England. Sometimes the five books were bound together. When space did not permit, the books were shipped separately and bound in England.

That spring William and Miles were pleased to see their old friend, John Frith. Still as tall and gangly as ever, he sat on a crate in William's tiny room with his long legs almost touching his chin. "I bring you greetings from Martin Luther," he said. "We met with Ulrich Zwingli and other church leaders in Marburg to discuss the meaning of Christ's presence at the Lord's Supper."

John told them about a young Scottish reformer named Patrick Hamilton, who lived in Marburg a few years ago. Last year Patrick was burned at the stake in Scotland, but not before putting together a collection of Bible passages in Latin to illustrate justification by faith. John translated this book into English, and it became popular with the people of England, who called it *Patrick's Places.*

When Master Packington made his monthly report, he told William that the recent printing of the New Testament was selling faster than any other merchandise. "Of course, our friendly clergymen are not pleased. They cry out that there are a thousand heresies in it."

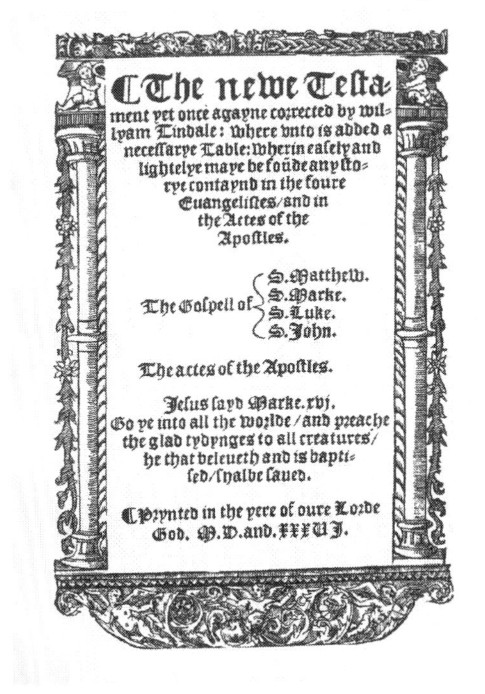

The newe Testament yet once agayne corrected by Willyam Tindale: Where unto is added a necessarye Table: wherin easely and lightelye maye be foũde any storye contaynd in the foure Evangelistes/and in the Actes of the Apostles.

The Gospell of S. Matthew. S. Marke. S. Luke. S. John.

The actes of the Apostles.

Jesus sayd Marke. xvj.
Go ye into all the worlde/and preache the glad tydynges to all creatures/ he that beleveth and is baptised/shalbe saved.

Prynted in the yere of oure Lorde God. M.D. and. XXXVJ.

The 1534 New Testament

William grinned. "I have seen what they call heresies. They scan the translation so closely that if a single 'i' lacks a prick over his head, they number it to the ignorant people for a heresy. If they took the same pains in translating the Bible, as they take in criticizing this translation, I suppose that they could have translated most of the Bible by now!"

"Ah, but that is something they will never do," said Packington. "They are saying that it is not possible to translate the Scripture into English and further, that it is not lawful for the lay people to have it in their mother tongue. They say it will make them all heretics!"

William waved his pen impatiently. "You've been reading too many essays by Thomas More."

"It seems that Sir Thomas More is angry that you use the word *elder* for the Greek word *presbuteros*. He wants you to translate it as *priest*.

"But the Greek word for priest is *hieros*, and it's important to show that the word is different. Surely they understand that an elder is just as likely to be the minister to a congregation."

"Ah, there's another heretical word. Sir Thomas does not like *congregation* either. He wants you to say *church*.

"He is splitting hairs!"

"No, it makes a difference. How could the Church of Rome threaten people with excommunication if Christ's bride was the people who make up the congregation, rather than the Pope and all his bishops?"

"But Erasmus, himself, translates *ekklesia* into Latin as *congregatio* or congregation. In the Greek it describes a community of people. Look here in the book of Acts."

Packington placed his large hand on William's shoulder. "My friend, I believe your translation is correct and Sir Thomas More is wrong, but beware that he violently opposes you."

The English merchants in Antwerp enthusiastically supported William's translations since few of them remembered their schoolboy Latin. "The more books in English the better!" one merchant told him heartily.

"But how can a person who was never trained in such things read the Bible?" another man asked.

William took a printed Pentateuch from his pocket and laid it on the table. "First, we must ask God's help, and then we should search for both the good and bad examples."

He opened the book to Genesis. "For example in these stories, note the weakness of Jacob's children and even the sin in them, and then see how God through their own wickedness saved them. Simply read it for yourself and think that every syllable pertains to your own self."

The man took up the book and peered at it closely. He read, "In the beginning God created heaven and earth. The earth was void and empty, and darkness was upon the deep, and the spirit of God moved upon the water. Then God said: let there be light and there was light."

"Why, this is plain English!" he exclaimed. "I can do what you say." He motioned to hand the book back, but William shook his head.

"Keep it for yourself. It is a book worthy to be read day and night and never to be out of your hands."

Chapter 17

Now that thou mayest read Jonas fruitfully and not as a poet's fable, but as an obligation between God and thy soul, as an earnest penny given thee of God, that he will help thee in time of need, if thou turn to him and as the word of God the only food and life of thy soul, this mark and note.

--William Tyndale in *The Prologue to the Prophet Jonas*

Jonah

Augustine Packington stamped snow from his boots as he closed the door against the icy wind. "Greetings Master Tyndale," he called in his booming voice.

William strode forward to greet his friend. "What news from England?"

"Just as cold as Antwerp," Packington replied. "Though Archbishop Warham is trying to make it a good deal warmer for our brethren. The English Scripture and your other books are abolished. He made a list of heresies found in them, and the first heresy is *faith only justifieth.*"

"In his eyes, St. Paul would be a heretic as well," said William wryly.

"Aye, and I think your newest book about the *Practice of Prelates* was the last straw. The officials printed placards denouncing your books and punished merchants for selling them. They arrested your brother, John, and several others in November and gave them large fines and public penance."

William frowned in worry. "What kind of penance?"

"They were made to wear your books tied around their necks and tacked all over their cloaks. On their heads they wore bishop caps made of cardboard with the words *pecasse contra mandata regis*, 'I have sinned against the commandments of the king.' Then they were forced to throw the books in a great bonfire."

William stared into the flames of the fireplace nearby. So much burning. Would that God might rekindle the truth.

William began work on the translation of the Old Testament book of Jonah. Just as Jonah was called to preach to Ninevah 'wherein there is a multitude of people, even above an hundred thousand that know not their right hand from their left,' William felt called to bring the Word of God to his own nation. Jesus, himself, referred to the book of Jonah. William would publish it as a pamphlet that could reach many readers.

In the prologue William wrote of the need for Christians to grow in the Lord "in the spirit, love and in the deeds thereof, as young children must have time to grow in their bodies." It was an important exhortation to the growing number of believers in England.

John Frith and his young wife came to the Low Country when England became unsafe for them. John helped William with his translation and proofing. These were some of the happiest days of William's exile as the work of translation sped forward with the skill and encouragement of John.

William printed the booklet at the Antwerp print shop

of Martin de Keyser. There he met a young man named George Joye. George was speechless when Martin de Keyser introduced William to him. He grasped William's hand warmly. "It is an honor, sir, to meet the man who brought the Bible to England. When I was at Cambridge there was hardly a student who had not read a smuggled copy."

"The Christian faith is still a popular topic at Cambridge?" William asked.

"It is still a greenhouse for true religion," George reported. "The authorities, however, make regular spectacles of punishing those guilty of owning a Bible. I was forced to leave, but I am trying to perform a profitable service in exile." He snatched up a freshly printed page for William to see. "This is my English translation of Isaiah from the Latin, and last year I printed the Psalms."

"This is excellent," said William.

The two men enjoyed their meetings at the print shop. They spoke of men they both knew from Cambridge. They discussed difficult problems with translation. One day George brought in a manuscript for William's approval. As William read it, he was dismayed to learn that George did not believe in the resurrection.

Without thinking, William said, "George, you have a marvelous imagination about the word *resurrection.*"

The young man scowled. "I take it to mean the state of the soul after departing from the body."

William bent over a proof and corrected a printing error before he replied. "If what you say is true, why does Paul teach in I Corinthians that 'the dead shall be raised imperishable'? Look in the Gospel of St. John when Christ says that the time shall come in which all that are in the graves shall hear his voice and shall come forth: they that have done good unto resurrection of life, and they who have done evil unto the resurrection of damnation. Why, Christ himself was resurrected in bodily form."

George squared his shoulders defiantly. "What if some don't believe that Jesus was raised in the body? I would rather translate that as *they shall come forth unto very life*. There is no need for the word resurrection at all."

"But George, you cannot change Scripture to suit your own ideas."

George was silent. He snatched back his manuscript and left the print house. In the days that followed he no longer conferred with William. He frequently received envelopes from England and wrote letters of his own that he sent with a messenger. When messengers arrived, he would excuse himself to speak with them.

During Lent in 1531 John Frith left Antwerp to visit England. He learned that the authorities were seeking to imprison him for his publication of *Disputation of Purgatory*. In this book he masterfully answered Thomas More and others over the issue of Purgatory. He showed that Purgatory was not taught in the Bible.

When John returned to Antwerp, William remonstrated with him. "You must not risk your life by visiting England," he said sternly. "You have a wife and small children to consider."

John listened attentively. "I will not risk my life needlessly," he said.

With John's help, William expanded and published the prologue which he had written for his first New Testament. He entitled the booklet *The Pathway to Holy Scripture*.

"I'm publishing this booklet so that the principles of faith can be understood from the beginning," said William.

John brandished his copy of the booklet. "If these truths are understood, all the Scripture will be unlocked and opened before a person. We need to pray that the churchmen will stop corrupting the true meaning of the Scripture."

William laughed. "They do all things of a good zeal. They love you so well that they would rather burn you than that you should have fellowship with Christ."

The Tower of London

Chapter 18

"And this faith and knowledge is everlasting life, and by this we be born anew and made the sons of God... And this faith is the foundation laid of the apostles and prophets... And this faith is the rock whereon Christ built his congregation... And against the rock of this faith can no sin, no hell, no devil, no lies, nor error prevail.

--William Tyndale in the *An Answer to Sir Thomas More's Dialogue*

Faith Under Fire

Despite William's disapproval, John Frith visited England again. He planned to go secretly to some of the Christians to encourage their faith. William counted the days until he would safely return, but John did not return on the appointed day.

After days of tense waiting, William received a letter from John Frith. He was imprisoned in the Tower of London.

William wrote two letters to John. John's wife asked him to include that she was "well content with the will of God, and would not for her sake have the glory of God hindered." William marveled at her faith and courage. She did not want her husband to deny his faith, even at the risk of death.

William never received a response to his second letter. By the time his letter reached London, his friend had been burned at the stake.

John Frith was burned with a young man named Andrew Hewit. The wind blew the flames away from them so that they suffered for over two hours before they died. Bystanders heard John exhort his young friend to trust his soul to God who had redeemed it.

Another dear friend, Thomas Bilney, who first invited William to the White Horse Inn, was also burned at the stake. He was a professor of civil law at Cambridge University, but was condemned for teaching Scripture. As he was committed to the flames, he said, "I have had many storms in this world, but now my vessel will soon be on the shore in heaven."

William's grief spurred him on to work for the sake of the gospel. His countrymen needed to know that they had a heavenly Father who was drawing them tenderly to Himself.

William composed an answer to Sir Thomas More, who had published a bitter criticism of the English New Testament. William defended his choice of words such as *love* instead of *charity*, and devoted several paragraphs to defining *the church*. He wrote:

> Christ's elect church is the whole multitude of all repenting sinners that believe in Christ, and put all their trust and confidence in the mercy of God, feeling in their hearts that God for Christ's sake loveth them. And this faith they have without all respect of their own deserving, yea, and for none other cause than that the merciful truth of God the father, which cannot lie, hath so promised and so sworn.

At this time King Henry VIII sought an audience with William. He sent an emissary named Stephen Vaughan to find him. Some believed that the king wanted to offer William a good appointment and a seat in his council in order to persuade him to support his divorce.

Henry VIII

Vaughan wrote letters to Frankfurt, Hamburg and Marburg in an attempt to contact William. Though he did not find him, he learned a good deal of information about him. Those who had met William said that he knew Hebrew, Greek, Latin, Italian, Spanish, French and German, and whichever he spoke you might think it was his native tongue. Vaughan began to wonder if it would be possible to track down a man who could blend into any country he chose.

After several months of fruitless searching, he trusted his message to a letter and hoped somehow William would receive it. In his letter Vaughan offered safe conduct to England on the King's authority. William knew that England was not safe for him and did not answer.

Vaughan wrote to both the King and Thomas Cromwell. In Cromwell's letter he added:

> It is unlikely to get Tyndale into England, when he daily heareth so many things from there which feareth him. ...The man is of a greater knowledge than the king's highness doth take him for; which well appeareth by his works. Would God he were in England!

When William heard that Vaughan was near Antwerp, he sent him a message. He told the messenger to simply say that a friend of Vaughan's was desirous to speak with him. The messenger delivered his curious message, and

Vaughan said, "Who is your friend?" The messenger could only say that he did not know. He bowed respectfully and continued, "but if it be your pleasure to go where he is, I can lead you to him."

The message intrigued Vaughn. He hoped that he would have nothing to fear in Antwerp during daylight hours. He followed the messenger through the streets of the city, but he hesitated when the messenger began to go through the city gates.

"He is outside the city?" Vaughan asked.

"Only a little farther, sir."

Near the gates lay a field, where a man stood waiting. The man was small in stature and wore a grave expression. He greeted Vaughan politely. "Do you not know me?" he asked.

"I do not well remember you," Vaughan said slowly.

"My name is Tyndale."

"But Tyndale! fortunate be our meeting."

"Sir, I have been exceeding desirous to speak with you," William said as they shook hands.

"And I with you. What is your mind?"

"I am informed that the king's grace takes great displeasure with me for putting forth certain books, especially for the book named *The Practice of Prelates*. I only wanted to warn his grace of the shameful abuses practiced, which threaten the welfare of his kingdom. I hoped to show that I was a true and loyal subject and to honor God with my service."

"Your warning against Cardinal Wolsey has proved true," said Vaughan. "He fell out of favor with the king and it was shown that he cared more for his own wealth than for the church. I would think that the king's grace already perceives you to be loyal."

"Then you must tell him that as a Christian prince he should desire the Scripture in the English language. He is the only sovereign who has not given this privilege to his people," said William.

"I know that you love England, and its king and people. Won't you leave this exile and return to your country?" asked Vaughan.

William thought of his home and for a moment the idea of seeing the hills of Gloucestershire almost overwhelmed him. "That is my dearest wish, but it is necessary for me to remain here."

"But there is nothing for you here," protested Vaughan. "I have questioned those who know you and they say that you work in poverty and hunger. If you come to England you would receive a position from the king."

"No," William said. "I have important work to do here."

"Would it change your mind to know that the King has offered you safe conduct?"

"I regret that I cannot rely on such surety. I have seen that the clergy advise the king that promises made to heretics ought not to be kept."

"But the king does not call you a heretic!" said Vaughan.

"I respect his grace, but I cannot trust the clergy." William bowed politely and turned to go.

"Wait!" cried Vaughan. "Will you at least send a letter?"

William paused to consider. "I have just finished a work defending the New Testament against Sir Thomas More's book, and I will not put it in print until the king has seen it. I want his grace to know that I am not of such an obstinate mind as has been reported to him."

"Thank you," said Vaughan as he warmly clasped William's hand.

"We may meet again," William said.

The two men did meet again. Vaughan made a report to the king and by the time of the second meeting, Vaughan received a reply to his letter. In the reply, Thomas Cromwell made it clear that the king had changed his mind. He said that the book by Tyndale was full of slanderous lies. Reading between the lines, Vaughan knew that Cromwell was not speaking for the king, but for his counselors and Sir Thomas More. Curiously, Cromwell added a long postscript to the letter urging his friend to persuade Tyndale to return to England. Vaughan showed the postscript to William.

When William read, 'the king's royal majesty is so inclined to mercy, pity and compassion,' he felt tears rise to his eyes. "What gracious words are these!" he said. "I assure you if it would stand with the king's most gracious pleasure to grant only a bare text of the Scripture to be put forth among his people, like as is put forth among the subjects of the Emperor in these parts, I shall promise never to write more."

The third time the two men met, William gave Vaughan a copy of his newest book, called *An Exposition upon the First Epistle of John*. Vaughan thought it was excellent. "I hope you will write more like this."

"I'm working on the *Sermon on the Mount*. I have decided it is better to teach the plain gospel than to wrangle with churchmen," said William.

Vaughan shrugged. "You might receive great favor and avoid persecution if you preach only the gospel and don't meddle with the pope, bishops and other great men of the world."

"Ah, but true preaching is salting, and even the persons you speak of will not be left untouched if they are corrupt," William replied.

Chapter 19

And let love interpret the law: that thou understand this to be the final end of the law, and the whole cause why the law was given: even to bring thee to the knowledge of God.

–William Tyndale in the 1534 Prologue to the Old Testament

God's Love

Hundreds of boats lined the long quay of Antwerp. William walked past humble fishing smacks bobbing alongside the larger vessels of the merchants. On the opposite side the houses with their towers and curious high-sloping roofs came right up to the harbor.

In the growing mist William peered at the old fortress at the river's edge. It was called the Steen. There was a legend that it was the home of the giant Antigon who cut off the hands of those who did not pay his river toll. A Roman soldier named Silvius Brabo killed the giant and cast his hand into the river, thus giving the town the name of *Handwerpen* or Antwerp which meant *to cast the hand*. William imagined that he could cast the gospel from Antwerp, across the sea, and home to England. He grieved that the church in England no longer preached the gospel. Instead it burned those who tried to preach it.

The Steen in Antwerp

William thought of Richard Bayfield who helped take three large shipments of books to England. He was betrayed on his last mission and burned at the stake.

When William entered the print shop, he found Miles poring over a book. "I've been reading *Sir Thomas More's Confutation of Tyndale's Answer*," Miles said with a grimace. "He writes that the *evil sects,* as he calls us, spring out of Luther's works 'which like the children of the viper would now gnaw out of their mother's belly.' He calls your New Testament the father of them all by reason of your false translating."

"He doesn't mince words, does he?"

"Sir Thomas More has written hundreds of pages against you, my friend. He calls you a hell-hound and writes that you discharge a filthy foam of blasphemies out of your brutish beastly mouth."

"I've read the first half of his *Confutation* and I must say he is very good at name-calling. I believe he also called me a hypocrite puffed up with the poison of pride, malice and envy. At the same time, the worst he could accuse me of was translating the Greek word *metanoeo* as *repentance* instead of *do penance*."

"In your debate with Sir Thomas More you have the Scripture on your side, but Sir Thomas has the backing of King Henry VIII and the church. You will never win against him," said Miles.

"But I don't need to win, if only the people of England will understand the gospel."

"Be careful, William. More's venom is not spent on words alone."

As William finished reading the book by Sir Thomas More, he could hardly believe this was the same man who had written the book, *Utopia,* and seemed so logical and steady. More wrote about mild Thomas Hitton: "and now the spirit of error and lying, hath taken his wretched soul with him straight from the short fire to the fire everlasting. And this is lo sir Thomas Hitton the devil's stinking martyr, of whose burning Tyndale must make boast."

Thomas Hitton, who did not deny his Savior, even as he was burned at the stake. Yes, thought William, I will boast in such true Christians.

One rainy afternoon William sat in the paneled room of the English House, only dimly aware of the murmur of conversation around him. He was revising his prologue to the Old Testament which he hoped to publish this year. He wrote:

> And let love interpret the law: that thou understand this to be the final end of the law, and the whole cause why the law was given: even to bring thee to the knowledge of God, how that he hath done all things for thee, that thou mightest love him again with all thine

> heart and thy neighbour for his sake as
> thyself and as Christ loved thee.

He prayed that his countrymen would understand God's love for them. In his revision of Genesis, William sought to clarify the Hebrew word *b'rith*. In his first translation he used the English words *bond* and *testament,* but he felt he needed a better word.

Nearby the merchants were discussing a document, and William heard one man say, "It cannot be changed because it is a covenant."

Covenant. William reflected on the meaning of the English word. It had a closer meaning to *b'rith* because it contained the idea of a commitment that could not be changed. William wanted his readers to understand that God's covenant with His people was a relationship of love and loyalty that could not be broken.

A newcomer entered the sitting room and the merchants hailed him amicably. "Come sit with us and tell us the news from London," said one man.

The newcomer took a place by the fire. "It was a chilly trip today," he told the others. "But I've got some news that will kindle your spirits. King Henry still wants to divorce the Queen, and Sir Thomas More has opposed him."

William paused from his work and thought, "I agree with Sir Thomas for once!"

The merchant continued. "The king is determined to have his way, so Sir Thomas More has resigned as Lord Chancellor. They say that the king wants to break away from the Catholic Church of Rome and make an independent Church of England."

As the merchants turned to one another to discuss the astonishing news, William was lost in his own thoughts. Sir Thomas More had vigorously defended the false doctrines of the church at the request of the king, and now he was in the peculiar situation of having to choose between that church and his king.

By the time William's revision of the first part of the Old Testament reached the presses, Henry VIII had established himself as the Supreme Head of the Church of England. The merchants from England related strange stories of church lands seized by the crown and feisty abbots who saw their monasteries pulled down stone by stone when they lost the battle with the king. The merchant Augustine Packington brought a fresh story.

"King Henry married Anne Boleyn in a secret ceremony in January," he began with his voice barely above a whisper. "In September, she gave birth to a daughter, who was named Elizabeth. Did you ever hear the story of how one of your books almost got her ladyship in trouble with King Henry?"

"I heard that the new queen was a friend to reform, but I never heard this tale."

"This happened back when Wolsey was Cardinal. Lady Anne had a copy of your booklet called *The Obedience of a Christian Man*. She marked with her fingernail parts of it that she wanted the king to read. The story goes that she loaned it to one of her ladies-in-waiting. This lady had a suitor who in jest snatched the book away from her and began to read it himself. He liked the book so much, that he took it with him. Then, one of the Cardinal's spies saw him and confiscated the book. He gave it to Cardinal Wolsey."

"I wonder what Wolsey thought of that," said William.

"Ah, he planned to discredit Lady Anne, but she was too quick for him. She went at once to the king and told him about the places she had marked. She begged him to help her find this book which was so dear to her. Soon after, the Cardinal entered with the book, and the king demanded to see it himself. He found the places that Lady

Anne had marked and declared that this was a book for him and all kings to read! Wolsey was purple with rage."

William pondered what would happen when King Henry was the Supreme Head of the Church of England.

Chapter 20

"Here thou hast (most dear reader) the new testament or covenant made with us of God in Christ's blood."

--William Tyndale in the prologue to the 1534 New Testament

John Rogers

Miles Coverdale was called to a congregation in Germany and William felt lonely. Miles wrote frequently to his friend and even enclosed copies of sermons he preached. A portion of one sermon on the resurrection of Christ particularly moved William:

> Now though the fear of death be great in nature, yet is it overcome through the strength and greatness of the love which we bear unto him who is our life, even Jesus Christ. And albeit he was the life itself, yet pleased it him to suffer death for us. Seeing then that he alone died for us, we ought not to be ashamed; neither should it grieve us to die also for him, specially considering that the publishing of so excellent grace is committed unto us.

William tucked the sermon into his coat pocket along with his copy of the newest printing of the English New Testament. Martin de Keyser of Antwerp printed the book to be only six inches tall and four inches wide so that it could be easily hidden. William also included forty Old Testament passages so that all the Scripture readings traditionally read in church services could be understood in English.

As William turned into the courtyard of the English House, he almost collided with a young man wearing a chaplain's robe. The young man peered at William with an owlish expression. "William Tyndale?" he asked. "I have been looking for you. My name is John Rogers, and I am the new chaplain for the English House."

William gripped his hand warmly. "I heard that you were coming, and that you are from Cambridge. Did you know my friend Robert Barnes?"

The chaplain blinked self-consciously. "I never fell in with that lot," he explained. "Though I have heard there has been quite a stir about these new ideas of grace."

William grinned. "The ideas are not new. Saint Paul wrote about them fifteen hundred years ago."

The chaplain shrank a little in his cleric robes. "I was not the student of Scripture as you were at Cambridge, but I would like to know more."

"The best place to start is with the Bible," said William. "Here, take this copy of the New Testament in English."

The next day John Rogers hailed William as he was leaving the English House. His chaplain's robe was wrinkled and his cap was slightly askew. "I did not sleep at all last night for reading the English New Testament," he exclaimed.

Slips of paper stuck out from the book in odd places, and John eagerly opened to the first paper. "See here in the first chapter of John where it says that *the law was given by Moses, even so grace to fulfill it is given by Christ*. And then here in the fourth chapter of Romans *that everlasting life is the gift of God through Jesus Christ our Lord."* A piece of paper fluttered to the ground as John dived into another section.

William clasped John on the shoulder. "I see that you are on the path to learning," he said.

Over the next few months John Rogers began to help William with his translation. He worked hard to acquire the skills he needed.

One afternoon John found William checking his translation of Romans.

"Isn't it tedious to read it over and over?" asked John

"On the contrary! No man can read it too often or study it too well. I find that the more I search it, the more precious are the things I find in it."

"I understand," said John peering intently at the proofs. "I have found more joy in reading the Bible since I came here, than I ever had in all my years studying for the priesthood."

William smiled in encouragement. "When Romans is simply read by itself, it is such a bright light that it gives light to all the Scripture. Every Christian man should not only know it by rote and without the book, but also review it himself continually, as with the daily bread of the soul"

"Have you read the new essay written against you by

Sir Thomas More?" John took a paper from his pocket. "I copied a section that you might enjoy. Listen to what he wrote:

> Then have ye his [Tyndale's] introduction into St. Paul's epistle, with which he introduceth and bringeth his readers into a false understanding of St. Paul, making them, among many other heresies, believe that St. Paul were in the mind that only faith were alway sufficient for salvation, and that men's good works were nothing worth."

William laughed. "It would seem that our good Sir Thomas understands the book of Romans perfectly!"

John and William walked home by way of a street lined with shops. William was still thinking of his work on Romans, when John darted into one of the book stalls and came out holding an English New Testament. "Is this your work?" he asked in a strained voice.

William opened the cover and saw the mark of the Endhoven print house. "It's the pirated copy that George Joye was proofing," he said quietly. "After John Frith's death I did not have the heart to confront Joye about it." William shook off his somber mood. "It's just a little spice of covetousness and vainglory on the part of Joye. Christ teaches us that we should do nothing from strife, so I will not press my rights against George Joye."

Later that evening William heard a knock on his chamber door. John in his stocking cap and nightshirt stood in the hallway. "William, you have to see this. Joye removed the word *resurrection* from his revision of your New Testament!"

William took up the book and quickly checked several references. It was true. Joye had changed the word *resurrection* to *life after life*. "He does not believe that there is a physical resurrection after death," William explained to John. "Some fury must have driven him to make such alterations."

"The Greek word *anastasis* can only mean resurrection," said John. "Yet I notice the scoundrel did not put his name on the title page."

"It's like playing boo peep," William said. "It is lawful for anyone to translate and show his mind, but it is not lawful that someone shall by his own authority take another man's translation and change it at pleasure."

Many people assumed Joye's pirated New Testament was Tyndale's work and published with Tyndale's authority. William mourned the corruption of God's Holy Scripture. To warn his readers against the false translation, he wrote a second prologue to his New Testament to explain what had happened.

Chapter 21

Neither can actual sin be washed away with our works, but with Christ's blood: neither can there be any other sacrifice or satisfaction to God-ward for them, save Christ's blood.

–William Tyndale in the prologue to the 1534 New Testament

Henry Phillips

Amidst the picturesque towers and roofs of Antwerp, the trees shone orange and gold in their autumn colors. William walked along the quay and dreamed of all the places the merchant ships would be travelling: up the Thames to London or by way of the Severn to ports in Gloucestershire. Perhaps even now his revised New Testaments were being secretly unpacked from bales of cloth.

William felt a growing sense of accomplishment. He had translated the Old Testament from Genesis through the book of Nehemiah and Jonah. A few more years would see the completion of the entire Bible, if the Lord willed it. He thought of the satisfying work to be done in the Psalms.

At the same time William felt an urgency to secure the

safety of the work he had done so far. When John Rogers was called to serve a Protestant congregation in Wittenberg, Germany, William entrusted him with a copy of his Old Testament translations.

"If anything happens to me, I want you to prepare them for the press. I will know that my work is not in vain," he said as he handed John the heavy package.

William moved his lodging to the house of Thomas Poyntz. Thomas was an Englishman and relative of Lady Ann Walsh.

"Lady Ann sends her regards," he told William. "She instructed me to keep you safe from agents of the king and church who are looking for you."

William thanked him for his help and added, "I always remember the Walshes with thanksgiving in my prayers. They often send money for my support."

Thomas Poyntz encouraged William in his work. He provided a place for him to study and shielded him from distractions.

Several English merchants boarded at the Poyntz home. William enjoyed hearing news of his homeland, but especially anything that the merchants could tell him about the spiritual state of the people.

One merchant reported that the bishops and Sir Thomas More were questioning everyone they could find who had been at Antwerp.

"Why do they do such a thing?" asked William.

"All their questions are about a man named William Tyndale. They want to know where he stays, and how tall he is, and what he wears."

Thomas took William by the elbow and led him from the room. His tone was urgent. "You are in danger, William."

"Nonsense, Sir Thomas More doesn't care what I'm

wearing."

"Don't you understand?" interrupted Thomas Poyntz. "They are seeking a way to trap you or catch you somehow."

"But I'm not in England. Antwerp is not under their authority. Rest easy, Thomas, I will not take a step outside this safe city."

"How many people know your true identity?" asked Thomas.

"Only a few of the English merchants," said William.

"We need to warn them to keep your secret," said Thomas grimly.

Not all the merchants took the threat seriously. They had many acquaintances in Antwerp and they often invited William to join them for dinners with other merchants. At one such dinner, a tall, young man strode forward, and clasped William's hand.

"I desire to make your acquaintance, Master Tyndale," he said. "I have long heard that you dwelt in Antwerp and our host has kindly pointed you out to me."

William was amused. "What is your name, sir, and how came you to hear of me?"

The young man bowed grandly. "Henry Phillips at your service. As for hearing of you, everyone knows that the English Bibles that are sweeping our fair nation are the product of one William Tyndale, now abiding in Antwerp."

"I am surprised to hear it," said William. "I heard the Bibles were repressed."

Henry winked. "Ah, they are, but that makes everyone want to read them all the more." He motioned to his servant who brought him his bag. It was beautifully embroidered and contained only one flat object. Henry reached into the bag and pulled out with a flourish an English New Testament. It looked as fresh as the day it came off the press. "See, I have one, too."

William took the book and opened to *The First Epistle of St. John the Apostle*. "This is a wonderful book." He read: "For all that is born of God, overcometh the world. And this is the victory that overcometh the world, even our faith. Who is it that overcometh the world: but he which believeth that Jesus is the son of God."

He looked up in time to see a startled glance from Henry, who quickly covered it with a chuckle. "Ah, you will be converting all of us young men before too long," he cried.

William returned the book to his new acquaintance. "I hope you will be blessed by this book," he said.

Over the next few weeks, William saw much of the tall, young man. At every gathering of merchants that William attended, Henry was there. William took every opportunity to talk with him about the Christian faith. Henry always had his Bible with him, and William showed him verses in the Bible that he hoped would help him.

One evening they happened to meet in the market place, and William invited Henry to come home with him for dinner. After Henry departed, Thomas Poyntz seemed anxious. "I don't trust that young fellow. He comes to Antwerp with a fancy servant, but no one can tell what he does."

"Perhaps he has a secret business, like smuggling Bibles," replied William with a twinkle in his eye.

"Nay, I would know if he had any such business," said Thomas.

"He seems to be an honest man," said William with a shrug. "He is handsomely educated and desires to know more of the Scripture."

"I still don't trust the fellow. Yesterday he asked me to walk with him about the town and show him the sights, but he seemed to be talking of the kings' affairs as though to see if I would accept a bribe." Poyntz straightened his shoulders. "I am an Englishman. I would never take a bribe!"

The next day as William walked home from church, he spied the tall figure of Henry in the distance. Henry waved in recognition and lengthened his steps to join William. "I am glad that we meet again," Henry said. "I would like to discuss with you your methods of translation."

"I am on my way home. Why don't you come with me and I will show you my books."

Henry was delighted. He spoke with animation of his days in college when he tried to learn Greek but did not have the patience for it.

When they arrived at William's room, Henry eagerly looked through all of his books and papers. He caught up a proof from Genesis.

"The fish of the sea, the birds of the air," he read aloud. "This is quite poetic."

"I try to write as the people speak," said William. "I want them to understand the Bible because it is the very word of God."

Henry laughed awkwardly. "I wish I could believe that." For a moment the glance that rested on William seemed tortured. The next instant he smoothed away his furrowed brow with an exaggerated sigh. "I cannot fathom the mountain of work that I see before me. I could never stick to such labor."

That same week Thomas Poyntz announced that he must travel to Barois where he had business for six weeks. As he took leave of William, he cautioned his guest to be careful. "There are rumors abroad that the bishops will do anything to put a stop to the English Bibles. The merchants are alerted, and we want you to remain in this house as much as possible. If you are in need, Barois is only a day's journey from here, so do not hesitate to send me a message."

William thanked his host for his concern. He promised that he would stay as close to the house as possible.

The next day Henry Phillips came to visit at noon. William was pleased to see his friend. "You told me you were leaving Antwerp," he said.

Henry made himself comfortable in one of William's chairs. "I had business out of town," he said vaguely. "The deuce of it is that I lost my purse this morning coming over the passage between here and Mechlin, and wondered if you would be so good as to lend me forty shillings."

"I would be glad to," said William.

"Master Tyndale," cried Henry, "you shall be my guest today."

"No," said William. "I am going forth today to dinner, and you shall go with me and be my guest, where you shall be welcome."

As the two men prepared to leave, William motioned for Henry to go before him since the entryway was long and narrow. Henry made a gallant motion with his hand. "You are my host today so you must go first."

William stepped through the entryway and his friend followed behind. William was shorter than Henry and did not see the gesture the younger man made to two officers who were seated on either side of the door. Suddenly the officers sprang to William's side and each took him by an arm. "Master Tyndale, you are under arrest by the procurator-general under orders of the Emperor," one man announced firmly. William looked quickly behind him to see his friend, but Henry had disappeared.

Only after he was in prison did William come to understand the truth. Henry Phillips had betrayed him. He was in the employ of certain enemies who were determined to stop the English Bibles.

Phillips had left Antwerp to go to the court of Brussels to bring the procurator-general, who was the emperor's attorney, and several officers to arrest Tyndale. He set the officers near the door of the Poyntz' home and used the story about losing his purse as a reason to see William and lure him out of the house. He studied the lay of the neighborhood and knew that the long narrow entryway would provide an easy way to place William before him so that he could signal to the officers.

The officers later told Thomas Poyntz that they pitied Tyndale's simplicity, for when he was arrested he made no excuse or attempt to flee, but graciously accompanied the officers.

William was taken to the castle of Vilvorde which was eighteen miles from Antwerp.

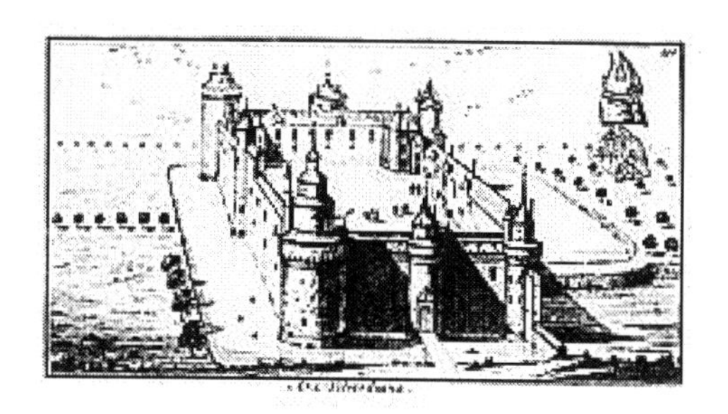

Vilvorde Castle

Poyntz hurried back from Barois only to find that all of William's books and papers were confiscated. He did everything he could to help William. He urged the English merchants to work on Tyndale's behalf. He appealed to the court at Brussels. He was impatient with the governor of the English House who was cautious about intervening. When William was still not freed after several weeks, Poyntz convinced Thomas Theobald, an emissary of the

English government, to write to Archbishop Cranmer.

Poyntz was beside himself with worry when weeks passed and nothing was done in response to the letter to the archbishop. He wrote to his older brother John who had been in the royal household for years and was lord of the manor of North Ockenden. He hoped that his brother could discuss the matter with the King. He closed his letter with these words:

> Brother, the knowledge that I have of this man causes me to write as my conscience bids me: for the king's grace should have of him at this day as high a treasure as of any one man living, that has been of no greater reputation. Therefore I desire you that this matter may be solicited to his grace for this man, with as good effect as shall lie in you, or by your means to be done, for in my conscience there be not many perfecter men this day living, as knows God.

Poyntz later learned more about Phillips. His father was a wealthy man. He sent his son with a large amount of money to pay a man in London, but Henry stole the money and wasted it in luxurious living and gambling. By the time he reached Antwerp, he had been a fugitive for many years. Clearly he was protected from the law at that time and someone provided him with money.

Nevertheless, Poyntz determined to save William.

Chapter 22

It is not enough therefore to read and talk of it only, but we must also desire God day and night instantly to open our eyes, and to make us understand and feel wherefore the Scripture was given, that we may apply the medicine of the Scripture, every man to his own sores...
--William Tyndale in the *prologue to the Old Testament*

Prison

Though the days were long, William's mind held a vast source of Scripture to ponder. His jailer liked to stay and talk with the prisoner when he brought his food. William spoke with him of the Christian faith. Soon the jailer was bringing his daughter to hear about the Bible from this gentle man.

One day the jailer found the two of them deep in conversation.

"Who dried up the Red Sea? Who slew Goliath?" said William. "Who did all the wonderful deeds which you read of in the Bible?"

The little girl's eyes lit up. "Our heavenly Father, of course."

"That is why we never need to fear. Our heavenly

Father can do wonderful things, and He cares for us, too."

The jailer came to respect William and said that if he were not a good Christian man, he knew not whom he might take to be one. The sincerity of William's life and the power of the Scripture were so great, that his jailer and his family came to believe that Jesus was their savior.

William sympathized with the apostle Paul, who spent a great deal of time in prison. In his mind he reviewed the translation of the fourth chapter of II Corinthians where Paul wrote:

> Wherefore we are not wearied, but though our outward man perish, yet the inward man is renewed day by day. For our exceeding tribulation, which is momentary and light, prepareth an exceeding and an eternal weight of glory unto us, while we look not on the things which are seen, but on the things which are not seen. For things which are seen, are temporal: but things which are not seen, are eternal.

Meanwhile Master Poyntz worked tirelessly to secure Williams's release. To Poyntz' joy, a letter arrived from Thomas Cromwell addressed to the two privy councilors in Brabant. He asked for Tyndale to be released and sent to England. Since one of the councilors was away on a diplomatic mission, Thomas Poyntz offered to carry the letter to him in Germany. He also carried a letter requesting that the councilor appoint a deputy.

At first the councilor was not friendly toward Poyntz. Poyntz convinced him to let him journey with him, and on the way the councilor changed his mind about Tyndale. He sent Poyntz back to Brussels with letters to appoint a deputy as well as a letter to Cromwell.

Poyntz raced back to Brussels to deliver the letters to

the council from both Cromwell and the councilor. The merchants then sent him to London with the reply to Cromwell's letter. Though his efforts took him away from his business, Poyntz stayed in London in order to take replies back to Antwerp.

A month from the day he began his work as a messenger, he delivered the letter from England to the Emperor's council in Brussels. He was told that Tyndale would be released to him.

Poyntz was preparing for the release of his friend, when he was suddenly arrested. Henry Phillips, worried that he would lose his payment for getting rid of Tyndale, accused Thomas Poyntz of being a heretic like Tyndale. He claimed that Poyntz was not representing England at all.

Poyntz remained under house-arrest. He was questioned by the procurator-general for five days and his case was heard over the next two months. Whenever the commissioners came to hear his trial, Henry Phillips followed them to the door.

As the weeks passed, the danger increased for Poyntz. When he learned that he was about to be transferred to a prison, he escaped and fled to England. He was banished from the Low Countries and his business was ruined.

The months passed and William still did not know what the authorities would do. Since he needed warmer clothing for the winter months, the jailer supplied William with paper and pen so that he could write a letter to the commissioner. William wrote:

Autumn 1535, Vilvorde Castle

> I believe, right worshipful, that you are not unaware of what may have been determined concerning me. Wherefore I beg your lordship, and that by the Lord Jesus, that if I am to

remain here through the winter, you will request the commissary to have the kindness to send me, from the goods of mine which he has, a warmer cap; for I suffer greatly from cold in the head, and am afflicted by a perpetual catarrh, which is much increased in this cell; a warmer coat also, for this which I have is very thin; a piece of cloth too to patch my leggings. My overcoat is worn out; my shirts are also worn out. He has a woolen shirt, if he will be good enough to send it. I have also with him leggings of thicker cloth to put on above; he has also warmer night-caps. And I ask to be allowed to have a lamp in the evening; it is indeed wearisome sitting alone in the dark. But most of all I beg and beseech your clemency to be urgent with the commissary, that he will kindly permit me to have the Hebrew Bible, Hebrew grammar, and Hebrew dictionary, that I may pass the time in that study. In return may you obtain what you most desire, so only that it be for the salvation of your soul. But if any other decision has been taken concerning me, to be carried out before winter, I will be patient, abiding the will of God, to the glory of the grace of my Lord Jesus Christ: whose Spirit (I pray) may ever direct your heart. Amen

W. Tindalus

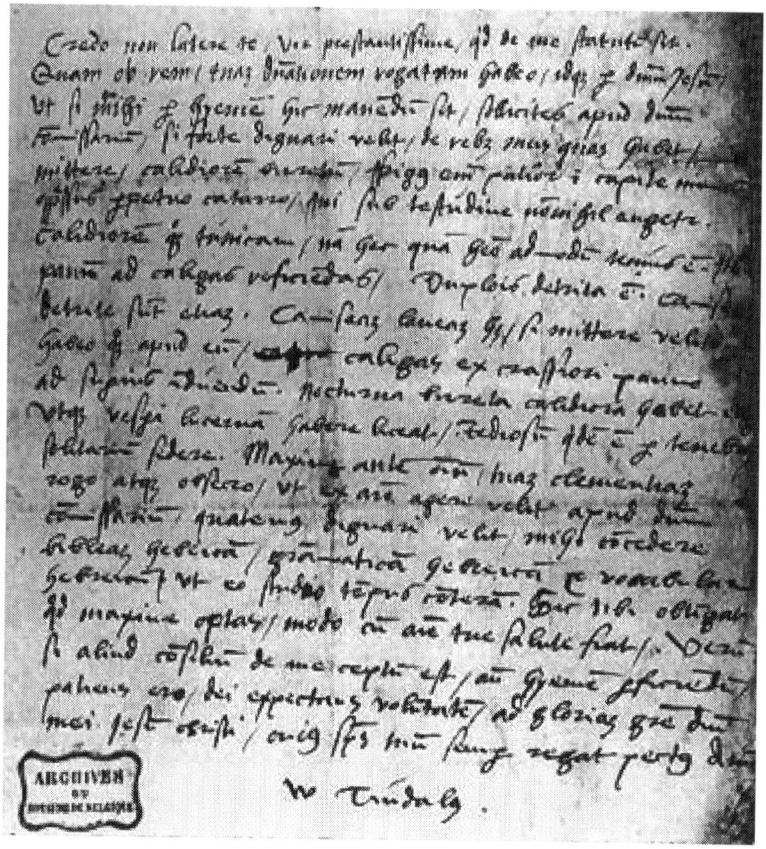

Tyndale's letter

Stephen Vaughan, the man who had tried to persuade William to return to England, wrote to Cromwell for his help. He wrote: "If now you send me but your letter to the privy council, I could deliver Tyndale from the fire, so it come by time, for else it would be too late."

Sadly, the letter never came. Perhaps the king and his council were preoccupied with other things. On May 19, 1536 Queen Anne, who had once shared Tyndale's book with the king, was beheaded. Among the possessions that she left to her daughter Elizabeth was an English New

Testament translated by William Tyndale.

Two months later Sir Thomas More met the same fate. As Lord Chancellor, he had sent many to the stake for denying the authority of the Pope. Now his loyalty to the Pope led to his own death.

The next month, in early August 1536, William was marched from his cell to a carriage which took him to a public ceremony. He was dressed in priestly garments and placed on a stage. A bishop and two prelates stood nearby. Many prominent churchmen attended the ceremony, as well as citizens from the surrounding area.

The bishop came forward and scraped his hands to symbolize the removal of the anointing oil. Bread and wine for the Mass, which were placed in front of William, were ceremonially removed. Finally, his priestly garments were taken from him. In the eyes of the Roman Church, William was no longer a priest.

After the ceremony, he was handed over to the procurator-general who would try him for offenses against the Emperor. Since this was a heresy case, a court of justice was not required. Instead, scholarly churchmen formed a commission to investigate his testimony and writings. It took several months to judge his writings because they had to be translated into Latin.

William was surprised to see Henry Phillips accompanying his inquisitors to the hearings. Phillips only once gave a sign of recognition. Their eyes met and William saw only hatred there.

William was offered an advocate and a procurator but he refused. He said that he would make an answer for himself.

Over a dozen lawyers and doctors of theology came to examine William during his imprisonment. He answered their questions and quoted the Bible to show his views. One scholar wrote three books in the process of disputing William's teaching. For his part, William wrote a book in Latin called *Sola fides justificat apud Deum* or *Only faith justifies before God*. Though there was common ground, William could not agree with his inquisitors in matters of justification by works and matters of Church practice which were based on tradition rather than the Scripture.

At last William grew weary of the long procession of lawyers, friars and doctors who questioned him in Latin. More keenly than ever he missed England. Alone in his cell he recalled his days climbing Nibley Knoll with his brother Edward and his time in Oxford and Cambridge exploring the Scripture with his friends.

As the weeks wore on, William asked the commission to send English clergymen to examine him. His request was granted. There were many English churchmen loyal to the Pope who lived in the Low Countries. They had fled England when Henry VIII broke with the Catholic Church. They were brought in to question William. By the end of the examination even the Procurator-general, who was a ruthless man, admitted that Tyndale was scholarly, godly and good.

Thomas Cromwell

Chapter 23

We are persecuted; but are not forsaken. We are cast down; nevertheless we perish not. And we always bear in our bodies the dying of the Lord Jesus, that the life of Jesus might appear in our bodies....For we know that he which raised up the Lord Jesus, shall raise up us also by the means of Jesus.

--II Corinthians as translated by William Tyndale

Standing Steadfast

Though William submitted his defense to the courts, it seemed that no reason would serve. His old friends, Sir John and Lady Ann Walsh, did their best from England to get William released from prison. Sir Thomas More was succeeded as chancellor by Thomas Cromwell. Unlike More, he was sympathetic to Protestant reform. He also worked to set Tyndale free by contacting the governor of the prison. He was not successful.

In prison William often thought of his friends who had died for their faith. There were Thomas Hitton, Thomas Bilney, John Frith and others. They were faithful to the Lord even unto death.

William was condemned by the emperor's decree made in the assembly at Augsburg. The official crimes of William

Tyndale were recorded:

First: He maintains that faith alone justifies.

Second: He maintains that to believe in the forgiveness of sins and to embrace the mercy offered in the Gospel, is enough for salvation.

Third: He avers that human traditions cannot bind the conscience, except where their neglect might occasion scandal.

Fourth: He denies the freedom of the will.

Fifth: He denies that there is any purgatory.

Sixth: He affirms that neither the Virgin nor the Saints pray for us in their own person.

Seventh: He asserts that neither the Virgin nor the Saints should be invoked by us.

On the day of the execution, the jailer and his daughter found William in prayer. Through the door they heard him speaking softly: "Jesus Christ our Lord and only savior: unto whom and unto God our Father through him, and unto his Holy Spirit, that only purgeth, sanctifieth and washeth us in the innocent blood of our redemption, be praise for ever. Amen."

When the door opened William lifted his head. His eyes were peaceful. "God will see me through whatever trials I must face." The jailer and his daughter wept as William spoke. Before he was led away to execution, William gave the jailer a letter for Thomas Poyntz, his faithful friend.

As William followed the prison guard, the words of the Scripture came to him. "I suffer trouble, as en evil doer, even unto bonds. But the word of God is not bound. Therefore I endure all things, for the elect's sake, that they might obtain that salvation which is in Christ Jesus, with eternal glory."

In Vilvorde, on October 6, 1536, William Tyndale was taken to the place of execution. Before the assembled crowd he was calm. As he was tied to the stake, he prayed with a strong voice, "Lord! open the king of England's eyes." He was then strangled by the hangman so that he would not have to suffer from the fire, and his body was burned at the stake. Though his life was brought to an end, the work he began lived on in the lives of thousands who could now read the Scripture for themselves.

Tyndale's Death
from **Foxe's Book of Martyrs**

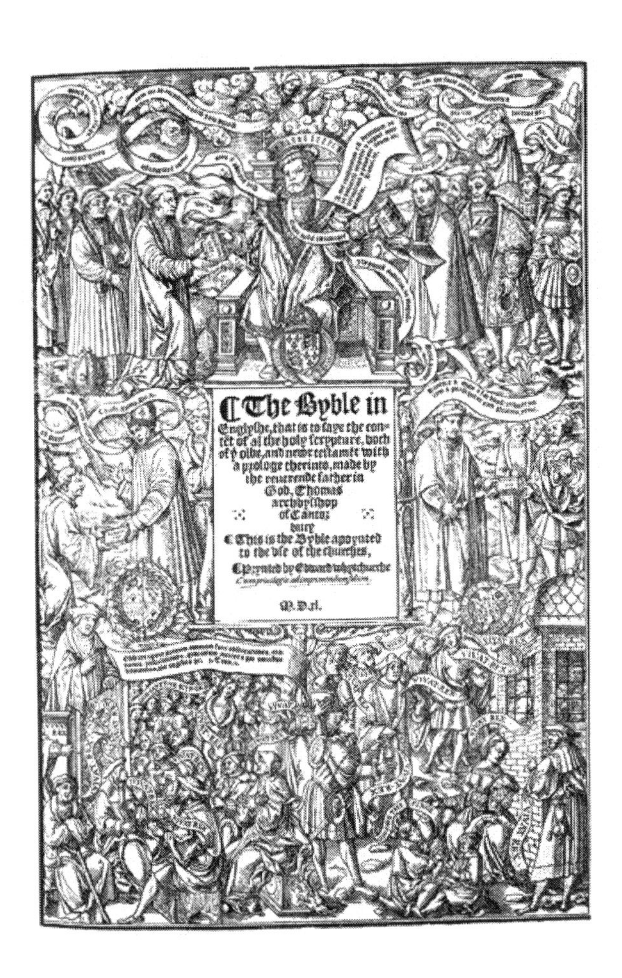

The Great Bible with the portrait of Henry VIII at the top

Epilogue

Believe nothing except God's word bear record,
that it is true.
—William Tyndale

The Monument to William Tyndale on Nibley Knoll

If you walk the Cotswold Way today, you can still see the monument to William Tyndale erected in 1866 on Nibley Knoll. Before his death, William Tyndale translated the New Testament and the Old Testament through 2 Chronicles, in addition to Jonah. Miles Coverdale, Tyndale's faithful friend, translated the remainder of the Old Testament and published the first complete English Bible while Tyndale was in prison. It became known as the Coverdale Bible. John Rogers, the friend entrusted with Tyndale's manuscript, printed the second complete English Bible in 1537. It was financed by the Grocers Company of London and the Merchant Adventurers of Antwerp. It was known as Matthew's Bible because Rogers published under the name of "Thomas Matthew."

Only three years after Tyndale's death, in 1539, King Henry VIII authorized Miles Coverdale to publish an English Bible. It became known as the "Great Bible" and was chained to the pulpit of every church. People crowded into churches to hear the Bible read. One man would stand and read until his voice grew weak, and then another would take his place. These readers were provided by King Henry VIII. Truly, the final prayer of Tyndale was answered: "Lord, open the eyes of the King of England."

The legacy of William Tyndale also continued in the enduring prose which his translations gave to the English-speaking world. To this day we read his work in the Authorized Version of the New Testament which is calculated to be nine-tenths from Tyndale. Common phrases such as *the salt of the earth*, *it came to pass*, *the twinkling of an eye* or *let there be light* were created by Tyndale. He captured the strong words and lilting rhythm of the English language in a way that would inspire future authors. His most important work, however, was his faithful striving to bring Scripture to his people.

Bibliography

Arber, Edward, ed., *The First Printed English New Testament*, London: Silverwood Printing Works, 1871

Arber, Edward, ed., *English Reprints No. 28, Roye and Barlow: Rede Me And Be Not Wroth*, London: 1871

Coverdale, Miles, *Works and Translations of Bishop Coverdale; Original Letters of the English Reformation 1537-1558*, 2 vols; Parker Society

Coverdale, Miles *Zürich Letters 1558-1602*, Parker Society

Daniell, David, *William Tyndale: A Biography*, New Haven: Yale University Press, 1994

Dickens, A. G. *The English Reformation*, London: 1989

Erasmus, Desiderius, *The Praise of Folly*, tr. Clarence H. Miller, London: Yale University Press, 1979

Erasmus, Desiderius, *The Enchiridion of Erasmus*, Tr. Raymond Himelick, Massachusetts: Peter Smith, 1970

Erasmus, Desiderius, *Enchiridion Militis Christiani: An English Version*, ed. A. M. O'Donnell, Oxford, 1981

Foxe, John, *The Acts and Monuments of John Foxe*, 8 vols, 4th edn, ed. rev, and corrected by J. Pratt; intro by J. Stoughton, London: 1877

Mozley, J.F. *William Tyndale*, London: 1937 (source of English translation of Tyndale's letter)

Pollard, Alfred W., *Records of the English Bible*, Oxford, 1911

Pollard, Alfred W., ed. *The Beginnings of the New Testament Translated by William Tyndale 1525,* Oxford: The Clarendon Press, 1926

Tyndale, William, Daniell, David, ed., *Tyndale's New Testament: A modern-spelling edition of the 1534 translation*, London: Yale University Press, 1989

Tyndale, William, Daniell, David, ed., *Tyndale's Old Testament: Being the Pentateuch of 1530, Joshua to 2 Chronicles of 1537, and Jonah, In a modern spelling edition*, London: Yale University Press, 1992

Tyndale, William, *The Exposition of the First Epistle of St. John*, Antwerp, 1531

Tyndale, William, *The Obedience of a Christian Man*, 1528

Tyndale, William, *The Parable of the Wicked Mammon*, Antwerp, 1528

Tyndale, William, *A Pathway to the Holy Scripture*, 1530

Tyndale, William, *The Practice of Prelates*, Antwerp 1530

Tyndale, William, *An Answer to Sir Thomas More's Dialogue*, ed. H. Walter, The Parker Society, Cambridge, 1850

Acknowlegement:

A special thanks to Heather McPherson Carter for her tireless efforts in editing this manuscript

Made in the USA
Columbia, SC
18 February 2024